Tackling Inequalities in Health

An agenda for action

Edited by   Michaela Benzeval

Ken Judge

Margaret Whitehead

King's Fund

Published by the King's Fund
2 Palace Court
London
W2 4HS

Tel: 0171 727 0581

© King's Fund 1995

ISBN 1 85717 088 1

A CIP catalogue record for this book is available
from the British Library

Distributed by Bournemouth English Book
Centre (BEBC)
PO Box 1496
Poole
Dorset
BH12 3YD

Designed and printed in Great Britain
by Intertype

Contents

Boxes, figures and tables

Notes on contributors

Sir Donald Acheson KBE is a former Chief Medical Officer for England and a Visiting Professor in International Health at the London School of Hygiene and Tropical Medicine.

Michaela Benzeval is a Senior Research Officer at the King's Fund Institute working in the area of equity in health and health care.

Richard Best OBE has been Director of the Joseph Rowntree Foundation since 1988. Prior to that he was Director of the National Federation of Housing Associations. Between 1984 and 1991 he acted as Secretary to the Duke of Edinburgh's Inquiry into British Housing and was an adviser to the House of Commons Environment Committee in 1993.

John Fox is the Chief Medical Statistician and the Deputy Director of OPCS. He is also a Visiting Professor in Epidemiology at the London School of Hygiene and Tropical Medicine. His previous position was Professor of Social Statistics and Director of the Social Statistics Research Unit at City University.

Ken Judge has been Director of the King's Fund Institute since it was established in 1986. Prior to that he was Deputy Director of the Personal Social Services Research Unit at the University of Kent and Lecturer in Social Policy at the University of Bristol. He is a Visiting Professor of Social Policy at the London School of Economics and Political Science.

Joy Townsend is a Senior Scientist/Health Economist at the MRC Epidemiology and Medical Care Unit at the Wolfson Institute of Preventive Medicine.

Steven Webb is Programme Director of the Personal Sector Research Programme at the Institute for Fiscal Studies. He is a specialist adviser to the all-party Select Committee on Social Services and was a member of the Commission on Social Justice.

Margaret Whitehead is an independent health policy analyst, writer and editor, whose special interests include health promotion strategies and equity in health issues. Since January 1993 she has been a Visiting Fellow of the King's Fund Institute.

Foreword

The wide and increasing social differential in premature illness and death in Britain should be a matter for serious public concern. In 1995 it seems almost commonplace to repeat what has been known for at least twenty years (Brotherston, 1976; Townsend and Davidson, 1982), namely that in this country death rates at most ages (including childhood) are two or three times as high in lower as in upper social classes and that among the least well off this leads to an attenuation of life of at least eight years together with a corresponding increased burden of ill health and disability. Today the question is not whether these facts are valid but who cares and what can be done about them. In the circumstances, it is particularly unfortunate that the issue has become a party political football.

The plan for this book arose out of a meeting between Robert Maxwell, Chief Executive and Secretary of the King's Fund, and myself late in 1991. In my capacity as Chief Medical Officer I had just completed my eighth report (and the 133rd in the series) *On the State of the Public Health* (DoH, 1991). As it was to be my last, I examined some of the events in my own period of office against a longer perspective. My principal conclusion was that, although in general the nation's health had continued to improve, inequalities between the social groups had persisted as a serious and almost certainly increasing problem. As long ago as 1858, in the very first report in the series, John Simon had pointed out that such inequalities are almost certainly due to social and environmental deficiencies which can be remedied.

What then was to be done? The King's Fund agreed with me that, with a number of detailed reports of the problem from Britain and other European countries already on the table, the existence and scale of inequalities could be taken as read. What was now needed was to prepare, in advance of the next general election, an agenda of possible policies directed to the reduction of inequality in health. It was to be hoped that these might be taken into account by the various political parties.

The work recorded in this volume was completed during the period 1993 to 1995. It encompasses and builds upon the presentations and discussions at a King's Fund seminar held at Ditchley Park in September 1993, which focused particularly on the effects on health of poor housing, family poverty, smoking, and lack of access to health services. This has been supplemented at the request of the participants by additional material including brief reviews of the effects on health of unemployment, poor education and lack of facilities for childcare. An important additional feature is that the book provides a model into which can be incorporated initiatives with a positive influence on health at four degrees of proximity to the individual (Whitehead, Chapter 3 in this volume). These comprise:

- strengthening individuals;
- strengthening communities;

- improving access to essential facilities and services;

- encouraging macroeconomic and cultural change.

A range of practical suggestions is provided for each category of intervention together with a review of the evidence for their effectiveness.

I compliment the editors, Michaela Benzeval, Ken Judge and Margaret Whitehead, on transforming the Ditchley Park discussions and subsequent material into this excellent book.

The approach in *Tackling Inequalities in Health: An agenda for action* provides an interesting contrast to Sir John Brotherston's (1976) 'Galton Lecture' addressing the same issues in 1975. The picture drawn then seems identical to that seen today, namely a universal increment in mortality and morbidity as one descends the social scale, and an apparent steepening of the social gradient of mortality across the decades (1921–23 – 1970–72). The contrast lies in the suggested remedies. In John Brotherston's lecture these are limited exclusively to improvements in access to health services for the less well off. There is a clear inference that, with appropriate targeting of its services to the less well off, the activities of the National Health Service would of themselves, in due course, if not wipe out at least substantially reduce inequalities in health.

Today the Ditchley agenda provides a wider and more radical challenge to politicians. We now see that any successful effort to reduce inequalities in health must be based on a broad range of actions involving almost every aspect of society. The approach to a number of the policies which must be considered, such as the redistribution of income, the creation of jobs, investment in new and improved housing (here the report argues that the funding problem is not as problematical as is often thought) and health impact assessment, is controversial across the political parties; others – including further sanctions on tobacco, the establishment of preschool education and better childcare – are less so. But at present, sadly, there is little evidence that any of the parties sees inequalities in health as a priority issue.

So, in the spring of 1995 with party manifestos already being drafted, where do we go from here? As public policies rarely emerge in a vacuum it is fortunate that there is currently a lively debate on inequalities in health (BMA, 1994) and the widening gap between the rich and the poor and its consequences (Joseph Rowntree Foundation, 1995). An added sense of urgency is provided by recent evidence that in the 1980s mortality among men actually increased in some age groups for the first time for many years in some deprived areas (McLoone and Boddy, 1994; Phillimore *et al.*, 1994). But this debate includes not only the implications of the social gap for health, but also, as the health of the public can be regarded as an indicator of the health of society itself, its implications for the cohesion and stability of society as a whole. There may thus be an element of self-interest for everyone to try to ensure that all citizens should feel they have a chance of sharing in the available benefits of prosperity and improved health.

Although from the outside it may not always seem so, it is my view, based on my brief experience there, that Whitehall mechanisms are sufficiently flexible to meet almost any eventuality. Provided there is a clear expression of political will from the top and a sense of urgency (and these provisos are crucial), policies on a topic which invoke even the whole spectrum of central government can emerge smoothly and quickly. A recent example was the work of the Whitelaw Committee, which in 1987 produced a comprehensive portfolio of policies at speed and with minimum fuss involving almost every government department in answer to a crisis of public confidence about AIDS. And who will say that it is less important that the suffering and waste associated with inequalities of health should be addressed?

The contents of this book set out evidence on which at least initial policies both at central and local government level might be based. But no-one would claim that scientific knowledge in this area is yet complete. The Royal Commission for Environmental Pollution, which celebrates its twenty-fifth anniversary this year, has produced an impressive array of studies over its lifetime. Many of these, such as the recommendation to remove lead from petrol, have led to significant changes in policy. I conclude that in respect of inequalities of health a standing Royal Commission along similar lines might serve to help clarify the remaining issues and sustain momentum.

E.D. Acheson

Social class	Classification
I	Professional occupations, e.g. doctors and lawyers
II	Managerial and technical occupations, e.g. teachers and senior administrators
IIIn-m	Skilled non-manual occupations, e.g. shop assistants and clerks
IIIm	Skilled manual occupations, e.g. brick layers, cooks and coal miners
IV	Semi-skilled occupations, e.g. bus conductors and postmen
V	Unskilled occupations, e.g. porters, cleaners and labourers

Socioeconomic group

An alternative occupational classification – socioeconomic group – was developed in 1951. This identified seventeen unranked groups such that each one contained people whose social, cultural and recreational standards and behaviour were similar. For most analytical purposes these seventeen groups are collapsed into six, which are set out below.

Socioeconomic group	Classification
1	Professional workers, e.g. accountants, doctors and lawyers
2	Employers and managers, e.g. managers in industry and commerce and farm owners
3	Intermediate and junior non-manual workers, e.g. nurses, teachers, technicians, clerks and shop workers
4	Skilled manual workers, e.g. bus drivers, plumbers and foremen
5	Semi-skilled manual workers, e.g. agricultural and catering workers
6	Unskilled manual workers, e.g. labourers, cleaners and porters

Standardisation

Standardisation is the method used to remove the effects of confounding factors, usually age and sex, when comparing two or more population groups.

Standardised mortality ratio (SMR)

The standardised mortality ratio is the ratio of the number of deaths observed in a specific group to the number expected if the group had the same age and sex composition as the standard population, generally the national average. This enables comparisons to be made between different groups, having taken account of differences that are the result of different age and sex structures. In each case 100 is the national average ratio. Groups with ratios less than 100 are healthier than the average; more than 100 they are less healthy.

Abbreviations

AHA	Area Health Authority
AIDS	Acquired Immune Deficiency Syndrome
ASH	Action on Smoking and Health
BMA	British Medical Association
CAPT	Child Accident Prevention Trust
CSJ	Commission on Social Justice
CSO	Central Statistical Office
DE	Department of Employment
DHA	District Health Authority
DHSS	Department of Health and Social Security
DHSSNI	Department of Health and Social Services Northern Ireland
DoE	Department of the Environment
DoH	Department of Health
DSS	Department of Social Security
DTI	Department of Trade and Industry
EC	European Community
EHCS	English Housing Conditions Survey
FHS	Family Health Services
FHSA	Family Health Services Authority
GHS	General Household Survey
GP	General Practitioner
HALS	Health and Lifestyle Survey
HBAI	Households Below Average Income
HCHS	Hospital and Community Health Services
HEA	Health Education Authority
ILO	International Labour Office
IPPR	Institute for Public Policy Research
JCC	Joint Consultative Committee

LA	Local Authority
LS	Longitudinal Study
MPC	Medical Practices Committee
NAO	National Audit Office
NCE	National Commission on Education
NCH	National Children's Homes
NCOPF	National Council for One Parent Families
NHS	National Health Service
NHSE	National Health Service Executive
NIC	National Insurance Contributions
OECD	Organisation for Economic Co-operation and Development
OPCS	Office of Population Censuses and Surveys
PSBR	Public Sector Borrowing Requirement
RAWP	Resource Allocation Working Party
RCP	Royal College of Physicians
RHA	Regional Health Authority
RUHBC	Research Unit in Health and Behavioural Change
SCOPH	Standing Conference on Public Health
SMR	Standardised Mortality Ratio
UK	United Kingdom
UNICEF	United Nations Children's Fund
USA	United States of America
VAT	Value Added Tax
WHO	World Health Organization
WRR	Scientific Council for Government Policy, The Netherlands

Summary

The international evidence on inequalities in health is compelling. People who live in disadvantaged circumstances have more illnesses, greater distress, more disability and shorter lives than those who are more affluent. Such injustice could be prevented, but this requires political will. The question is: can British policy makers rise to the challenge?

Health inequalities are an endemic characteristic of all modern industrial societies, but the size of the differential varies between countries and over time, indicating that there is nothing fixed or inevitable about having such a health divide. Of particular concern is the fact that social divisions have been growing rapidly in Britain in recent years.

In recognition of the health-damaging consequences of this trend, the King's Fund responded positively to a suggestion by Sir Donald Acheson, the former Chief Medical Officer for England, that the time was right to consider practical policy options for tackling inequalities in health. As a result, the Fund organised a seminar at Ditchley Park in September 1993, which brought together a wide range of people – from central and local government, health authorities and voluntary organisations, to universities and research institutes, professional associations and the media – to examine the policy options and to identify priorities for action in tackling inequalities in health.

Tackling Inequalities in Health reflects the nature and spirit of the discussions that took place at Ditchley Park. It does not try to add to the voluminous literature that has already documented evidence about the nature of the problem, but instead it aims to make the case that something can and should be done about it. Many of the underlying socioeconomic causes of health inequalities are amenable to changes in public policy. The objective is to outline a number of practical and affordable ways in which the situation could be substantially improved if the political will existed to recognise that tackling inequalities in health is a fundamental requirement of social justice for all citizens.

Extent and nature of inequalities in health

In Britain death rates at all ages are two to three times higher among disadvantaged social groups than their more affluent counterparts. Most of the main causes of death contribute to these differences, and as a result, people in the least privileged circumstances are likely to die about eight years earlier than those who are more affluent. People living in disadvantaged circumstances can also expect to experience more illness and disability.

There is nothing new or unique about the existence of inequalities in health. They were first documented in Britain in the 1860s and are evident in countries across the developed world. Evidence that such inequalities exist is based on numerous studies that measure health and socioeconomic circumstances in a variety of ways. They include data on mortality, morbidity, self-reported health status and professionally measured fitness, from official statistics, cross-sectional and longitudinal surveys and numerous small-scale studies.

What is particularly worrying, however, is that economic inequality appears to be growing more quickly in Britain than at any time since the Second World War. Moreover, during the 1980s social divisions accelerated at a rate not matched for such a sustained period by any other rich industrialised country. Not surprisingly, the impact that this increase has had on health is now beginning to emerge. Death rates in some of the most disadvantaged areas in Britain not only worsened in relative terms between 1981 and 1991 when compared with the most affluent areas, but among some age groups, such as young men, the rates actually rose. As death rates in Britain have been declining since the 1930s, this rise signals a new and disturbing development.

Explanations about the causes of inequalities in health are complex, but it is likely that a combination of factors is at work reflecting people's living and working conditions, their resources, social relationships and lifestyles. However, since much health-related behaviour itself is socially determined, it is people's circumstances that are the most important determinant of health.

What could be done?

A detailed review of interventions in various countries at different times, by Margaret Whitehead, suggests that policy initiatives that can influence inequalities in health exist at four different levels:

- strengthening individuals;
- strengthening communities;
- improving access to essential facilities and services;
- encouraging macroeconomic and cultural change.

Policies that attempt to strengthen individuals aim to change people's behaviour or coping skills through personal education and/or empowerment. General health education messages have had a limited impact on people from disadvantaged environments because the pressures of their lives constrain the scope for behavioural change. However, more sensitive interventions that combine education and support can have a positive effect on the health of people in disadvantaged circumstances if they are carefully tailored to their needs and combined with action at other policy levels.

Policies that aim to strengthen communities have either focused on strengthening their social networks or they have adopted a broader strategy that develops the physical, economic and social structures of an area. Such initiatives can, through involving the community itself in the determination of priorities, change the local environment, services and support systems in ways that promote equity in health.

Despite some successes, however, efforts to strengthen individuals and communities have had a minimal impact on reducing inequalities in health. Much greater influence is possible at the other policy levels. Some of the greatest gains in health in the past have resulted from improvements in living and working conditions – better housing, improved water supply and sanitation, safer conditions in the workplace, education, the alleviation of poverty and general provision of health and welfare services. Western countries must guard against changes that undo these successes. At the same time, further changes in these areas will continue to be needed to reflect the pace of social change.

Macroeconomic and cultural changes are also important determinants of health because they influence the overall standard of living in a country and its distribution; attitudes to women, minority groups and older people; and major environmental factors such as international pollution. Policies at this level have been shown to have differential effects on the various groups in society, creating major implications for tackling inequalities in health. For example, some of the early structural adjustment policies, to deal with countries in economic crisis, hit the most disadvantaged sections of the population hardest. Conversely, macroeconomic policies in various countries that have protected or improved the standards of living of poorer groups have had a beneficial impact on the population's health.

A worthwhile agenda for tackling inequalities in health must therefore include a strong focus on reducing poverty and a commitment to the careful monitoring of the impact of major public policies on health, particularly among the most vulnerable groups.

What should be done?

The more the determinants of health are recognised and understood the more inescapable is the conclusion that a person's health cannot be divorced from the social and economic environment in which they live. Factors that are increasingly recognised to be of critical importance and that shaped the thinking for the Ditchley Park seminar include:

- the physical environment, such as the adequacy of housing, working conditions and pollution;
- social and economic influences such as income and wealth, levels of unemployment, and the quality of social relationships and social support;
- barriers to adopting a healthier personal lifestyle;
- access to appropriate and effective health and social services.

In this book, an example of each factor – housing, income maintenance, smoking prevention and access to health care – has been selected to illustrate new policy initiatives that should form part of a strategy to tackle inequalities in health. We also examine in briefer fashion other policy areas – unemployment, education and childcare – that participants at the Ditchley Park seminar suggested should form part of any concerted attempt to tackle inequalities in health.

Housing

Richard Best highlights many of the housing problems facing Britain today. These include:

- the rapid rise in homelessness in the 1970s and 1980s among both families and single people;

- the large numbers of properties in bad condition suffering from problems such as damp, inadequate heating, infestations, poor design and lack of play space;

- the social isolation caused by high-rise blocks and the social segregation apparent in many deprived estates.

Such problems can have adverse effects on people's health. For example:

- people sleeping rough are three times as likely to have chronic chest conditions;

- families in bed-and-breakfast accommodation have higher rates of infections, gastro-enteritis, child accidents, parental stress, poor child development and nutritionally unsatisfactory diets;

- inadequate or unaffordable heating almost certainly contributes to hypothermia and excess winter mortality among older people;

- damp housing has been shown to cause respiratory and other illnesses in children and stress among adults.

A range of policies need to be developed that tackle these housing problems in ways that reduce inequalities in health. Investment in new social housing and improving the existing housing stock should be promoted as a matter of urgency. Similarly, community regeneration schemes should be introduced in areas of high deprivation to improve the environmental, economic and social structures of disadvantaged neighbourhoods. In addition, tax concessions should be given to private landlords to encourage the expansion of the private rented sector.

Such policies can be financed in a number of ways. For example:

- public housing could be transferred out of the public sector to local housing companies, which would enable capital to be raised to finance improvements to properties and estates without being constrained by the conventions of the PSBR;

- mortgage tax relief could be removed and the savings used to provide capital subsidies for housing associations and local authorities. This would enable them both to build more houses and to charge lower rents, which would in turn reduce the cost of housing benefits to the social security system.

Help is also needed for owner occupiers on low incomes, many of whom experience difficulties with their mortgage payments. The introduction of 'mortgage benefits' would not only reduce the large number of repossessions experienced in the 1980s, but would help to eliminate the poverty trap. One illustration of the absurdity of present arrangements is that for a family paying a rent of £70 per week an increase in gross earnings from £80 to £300 per week would leave them just £30 better off. The abolition of tax relief on mortgages would generate sufficient funds to finance this policy as well as the additional investments in social housing described above.

Family poverty

The latest evidence for 1991–92 suggests that families with children are over-represented at the lower end of the income distribution, comprising 57 per cent of households with incomes below 40 per cent of the UK average, but only 45 per cent of the total. There are three main causes of family poverty:

- unemployment;
- lone parenthood;
- low wages.

Michaela Benzeval and Steven Webb show that:

- a strong association between low income and poor health has been demonstrated across the developed world;
- in Britain, people in the lowest income quintile are four times as likely to report their health as not good as those in the highest income quintile.

Poverty can affect health in a number of different ways:

- income provides the prerequisites for health, such as shelter, food, warmth and the ability to participate in society;
- living in poverty can cause stress and anxiety which can damage people's health;
- low income limits people's choices and militates against desirable changes in behaviour.

The best way of reducing family poverty is to tackle its causes by ensuring that all people who wish to be economically active have access to well-paid jobs. Useful steps in this direction would include better training opportunities and improved childcare facilities, as discussed below. However, given that it is unlikely that all families will be able to escape from a reliance on benefits in the foreseeable future, the social security system also needs to be reformed.

Increasing child benefit would be one way of improving family income. However, it would not be a very effective way of tackling family poverty since a large investment would only result in modest increases in the income of poor families. A more cost-effective way of reducing family poverty would be to increase means-tested benefits such as income support and family credit. Other policies that would reduce some of the pressures on people with low incomes should include:

- tackling problems of low uptake of benefits;
- replacing the social fund loans scheme with a grants system;
- ensuring that all households have access to vital utilities – such as heat, light and water – without the threat of disconnection.

In addition, the drift to greater economic inequality that has been exacerbated by recent tax changes benefiting the most affluent needs to be reversed. Measures could include:

- abolishing the upper limit on employee national insurance contributions;

- restricting the value of the main personal tax allowances to the lowest rate, i.e. 20 per cent for all taxpayers;

- increasing the highest rate of income tax;

- shifting the balance of taxation away from spending and toward income.

Not only might these measures reduce inequalities in health but they would also raise the resources necessary to finance a comprehensive strategy to promote social justice and equity in health.

Smoking

Smoking-related diseases are the greatest single cause of premature mortality and excess morbidity in the UK.

Although the number of people who smoke has fallen substantially over the last three decades, this reduction has mainly occurred among more affluent social groups so that smoking is now predominantly a habit of people in disadvantaged circumstances. Joy Townsend shows that:

- three times as many people in unskilled occupations smoke compared to those from professional groups;

- particularly high smoking rates are found among people who are unemployed and young adults with children, especially lone parents.

Smoking increases the risks of most major killers such as lung cancer and heart disease. For example, smokers are twenty times more likely to die of lung cancer than non-smokers. Such diseases are much more prevalent among disadvantaged social groups. However, it should not be assumed that the health divide has a single cause. Substantial socio-economic gradients in mortality and morbidity exist among non-smokers. It is also important to note that behaviours are determined by the social environment in which people live, and so encouraging behavioural change requires much more than exhortation.

Policies to reduce smoking may include health education and cessation advice, controlling tobacco advertising, restricting the availability of cigarettes, creating smoke-free environments and increasing taxation on tobacco-related products.

- Health education and cessation advice have had a limited impact on smoking rates among the more disadvantaged social groups. However, these interventions can be made more effective by being made more sensitive to the pressures of people's lives and being backed up by wider policies to create a supportive environment.

- New resources should be invested in developing and evaluating innovative interventions, in health education, cessation support clinics and advice by primary care workers, targeted at vulnerable groups. Nevertheless, other wider strategies need to be adopted to have any major impact on smoking prevalence among the most disadvantaged groups.

- One priority for action is a ban on the advertisement and promotion of cigarettes and tobacco-related products. It is estimated that this would reduce smoking by approximately 7.5 per cent. In particular, given that young people are thought to be more influenced by advertising and that advertising is more prevalent in tabloid papers and on posters in disadvantaged areas, a ban would have most effect on teenagers and those with low incomes.

- A further priority is to increase the real price of cigarettes. This would reduce both the number of people who smoke and the number of cigarettes smoked by those who continue. However, the cost would fall disproportionately on people with low incomes and should not be lightly contemplated in isolation from a broadly based anti-poverty strategy.

The NHS

It is important not to exaggerate the role of health services in tackling health inequalities. It is equally important, however, that they do not abdicate those responsibilities which properly fall on them. Health care systems do have a useful even if relatively minor role to play in promoting social justice and equity in health.

Michaela Benzeval, Ken Judge and Margaret Whitehead argue that the Department of Health and the NHS at large have three key obligations:

- to ensure that resources are distributed between areas in proportion to their relative needs;

- to respond appropriately to the health care needs of different social groups;

- to take the lead in encouraging a wider and more strategic approach to developing healthy public policies.

Existing resource allocation mechanisms in the NHS have done much to address some of the historical inequities in health care provision, but further reforms are needed. A unified weighted capitation system should be introduced to ensure that all resources are allocated to areas in relation to the need for them.

In addition, as purchasing decisions are devolved to more local areas, two safeguards are required:

- substantial resources need to be top-sliced for local health authorities to enable them to take the broad population approach – to assessing needs, monitoring access to care and providing community-based services – that is required to deliver equitable services;

- a fairer system of allocating resources to GP fundholders needs to be established.

Evidence about equitable access to care in Britain is patchy. There is some highly aggregated evidence that implies the NHS does surprisingly well in ensuring that resources are distributed between social groups in proportion to their relative needs. On the other hand, this is countered by a number of small-scale studies that suggest that among a range of specific services and at local levels more disadvantaged social groups do appear to be under-served.

Perhaps most worrying, however, is how little is actually known about the social characteristics of patients and their response to treatment. The NHS needs to make much greater efforts to assess whether it is achieving equal access for equal need for all social groups. Local health authorities need to develop equity audits as a matter of urgency.

Where there is evidence that people with poor socioeconomic circumstances are inadequately served in relation to their needs, a new approach that empowers communities and individuals needs to be adopted. Some studies suggest that barriers to access to health care can be reduced through the introduction of more sensitive and appropriate community-based services.

The NHS should also take the lead in developing policies at both the national and local level to promote equity in health.

- At the national level, mechanisms are needed to facilitate interdepartmental co-operation and multisectoral action to tackle health inequalities. Health impact assessments should also be introduced to monitor the effects of all public policies on health.

- Equity-orientated health targets should be set to maintain a strong national focus on reducing inequalities.

- At the local level, the promotion of initiatives that develop structural links between different agencies can enable the health service to take part in policy making on issues that affect population health, such as the local environment, housing, education and transport.

Education, unemployment and childcare

A crucial step in tackling inequalities in health is the need to create opportunities for prosperous and fulfilling employment for all citizens. The causal link that runs from deprivation to poor schooling, unemployment, low earnings and poor health must be broken. We highlight four key policy initiatives that are required to help both the next generation of workers and those who currently find it most difficult to find opportunities in the world of work.

- Preschool education should be expanded, particularly for children living in disadvantaged circumstances, to give them a better start in life and to create greater equality of educational opportunity.

- Particular efforts are needed to increase resources for education in disadvantaged areas and to support those working there.

- Long-term unemployment should be tackled by improving education and training programmes, overhauling the tax and benefit system, and stimulating new patterns of working and entrepreneurship.

- The quality and quantity of childcare services in Britain need to be improved. The lack of provision of childcare facilities is thought to be a major cause of poverty, since it prevents women, particularly lone mothers, from taking up paid employment.

Conclusion

The underlying rationale for this book is the belief that observed social inequalities in health are amenable to purposeful policy interventions. The problem is well documented and the solutions become clearer every day. What is needed is a determined effort to mobilise the political will to create a fairer society that embraces all sections of the community.

Tackling Inequalities in Health sets out a practical agenda that represents a modest beginning. We cannot pretend that we have considered every possible strategy or that the precise health benefits that might flow from different interventions are clearly understood. What we do claim is that the problem of health inequalities is a real and substantial one that demands urgent attention. In particular, we commend the detailed recommendations contained in this book. But the package as a whole, or any particular proposal, is less important than that there should be a genuine commitment by policy makers to promote action which will improve the health prospects of those whose lives are blighted and shortened by avoidable and unacceptable disadvantage.

Now is a good time to start.

CHAPTER 1

Introduction

Michaela Benzeval, Ken Judge and Margaret Whitehead

I am not saying that people are equal; but that the tendency of all law-making and of all governing should be to reduce the inequalities.
Lady Glencora Palliser in *Phineas Finn* by Anthony Trollope

One of the aims of a modern society should be to ensure that every citizen has a fair chance of living a long and healthy life. This is not always possible. Some of the things that affect health – such as age, gender and genetic make-up – cannot be changed by individual choice or public policy. A much more serious problem is the very large number of men and women of all ages who are prey to premature death, disability or chronic sickness as a consequence of social circumstances which could be changed by purposeful public policy interventions.

It is one of the greatest of contemporary social injustices that people who live in the most disadvantaged circumstances have more illnesses, more disability and shorter lives than those who are more affluent. In Britain death rates at most ages are two to three times higher among the growing numbers of disadvantaged people than they are for their better-off counterparts. Most of the main causes of death contribute to these differences and together they can reduce average life expectancy by as much as eight years.

There is nothing new about social inequalities, nor are they unique to Britain. As Box 1.1 shows, study after study in large numbers of first-world countries has demonstrated that the more disadvantaged people's socioeconomic circumstances are, the worse is their health status. At every age the probability of premature death is enormously increased by adverse social conditions. Similar socioeconomic gradients are to be found in relation to disability and illness. Across the developed world, no matter how social status is measured, those in the most disadvantaged circumstances suffer worse health than all of those above them, especially those who are most advantaged.

What is particularly worrying, however, is the suggestion that one of the most significant indicators of disadvantage – economic inequality – appears to be growing more quickly in Britain than in any other advanced industrial society. For example, in a recent review of international trends, which included most of the countries of western Europe together with Australia, Canada, Japan, New Zealand and the USA, Atkinson reports that 'the UK stands out for the sharpness of the rise in recorded income inequality in the second half of the 1980s. This was unparalleled in the countries examined' (1994, p. 7).

Box 1.1: International evidence

Inequalities in health have been reported across the developed world. Premature mortality rates, illness and disability are all higher among the more disadvantaged sections of most countries' populations. A selection of evidence that demonstrates the substantial variations in health which exist between different social groups across a wide range of countries is set out below.

Australia

A comprehensive analysis of socioeconomic differences in health (National Health Strategy,1992) reported higher rates of mortality, morbidity and risk factors among the more disadvantaged sections of the population. Some examples include:

- children with no parents in paid employment are 25 per cent more likely to have a serious chronic illness than those with at least one parent in paid work;
- women with low incomes are 83 per cent more likely to suffer disability than those with high;
- men with low educational status are 150 per cent more likely to report poor health than those with the most education.

Belgium

In a survey of infant and maternal health in southern Belgium, strong gradients – based on an index of education, income and occupation – were found across a range of health indicators. For example, twice as many babies born to families with low social status (11.5 per cent) had low birthweights as those in the most advantaged social group (5.5 per cent) (Lagasse *et al.*, 1990).

Finland

A study which linked mortality data to census information found that a 35–year-old man with a basic education had a 50 per cent higher probability of dying before retirement age than someone with higher education (at least 13 years). The probability of a person in an unskilled occupation dying was about twice that of someone with an upper white-collar position (Valkonen, 1993).

France

A longitudinal dataset of mortality found that men with unskilled jobs aged 45–49 had death rates four times that of employees in high-status occupations (Desplanques, 1984).

Ireland

Significant differences in standardised mortality ratios exist between occupational groups. For example, in 1981, men with higher professional positions aged 15–64 had an SMR of 55, a third of the ratio of those in unskilled occupations (163) (Nolan, 1990).

Italy

A national morbidity survey conducted in 1983 showed social gradients – measured by both education and occupation – in health. For example, over twice the proportion of people with only elementary education (25.7 per cent) reported their health as not good as those who attended university (12.3 per cent) (Piperno and Di Orio, 1990).

The Netherlands

A review of evidence from a number of different Dutch datasets found substantially lower mortality rates and age-adjusted rates of reporting poor health among those with the highest levels of

Box 1.1: Continued

education. For example, in a nationally representative survey of 10,000 people, the age-adjusted rate of reporting health as not good by university graduates was only 64 per cent of the national average (Mackenbach, 1993).

Norway

A survey of adults aged 25–66 conducted in 1983 found that the proportion of men in unskilled occupations with chronic illness was 1.4 times that of those with high-status jobs. Twice as many women with unskilled jobs had cardiovascular illness as professionals. Linking mortality data to census information produced similar results. In unskilled occupations, men had an SMR of 118 and women 110 against 68 for men and 91 for women, with high-status jobs (Dahl, 1993).

Spain

A national health interview survey asked 30,000 adult respondents about their experience of chronic illness. The analysis was restricted to nine main conditions. For women aged 20–44 the age-adjusted number of conditions reported was 30.7 per 100 people in the highest decile of equivalent income and 45.5 in the lowest decile (Kunst and Mackenbach, 1994).

Sweden

A census-linked death registry for Sweden for 1961–79 enabled researchers to construct a measure of social class very similar to that used in Britain. Age-standardised death rates for men aged 20–64 were 27 per cent higher among semi-skilled and unskilled workers than among professional and managerial groups (Vågerö and Lundberg, 1989).

Switzerland

A survey of a representative sample of adults in Switzerland found that 'underprivileged groups', manual workers and those without any training had poorer health status – in terms of limiting health problems, serious illness or disabilities – than those from the upper classes or those who were well educated. For example, people in manual occupations aged 20–49 had over three times the average number of disabilities of those in the upper classes. Men in unskilled occupations aged 15–74 had an SMR nearly 60 per cent higher than professionals. The children of unmarried mothers had higher rates of perinatal and infant mortality and low birthweight across all social classes (Lehmann et al., 1990).

USA

A comprehensive analysis of a national sample of deaths in 1986 linked to questionnaires of kin found that people with low incomes or poor educational attainment had higher death rates than those who were rich or well educated. For example, the age-adjusted mortality ratio for white men with the lowest educational attainment was more than two and a half times higher than the comparable ratio for those with the highest level of education (Pappas et al., 1993).

Western Germany

A pooled survey of 40,000 people conducted between 1984 and 1991 found that, for both men and women, disadvantaged socioeconomic status – measured by a composite index of occupation, income and education – was significantly associated with a higher prevalence of myocardial infarction, stroke, diabetes mellitus and chronic bronchitis (Helmert and Shea, 1994).

A small selection of some of the key facts about the extent and nature of social inequalities in health in Britain is set out below and Chapter 2 provides a more comprehensive summary of the critical evidence.

- The total excess deaths in the most disadvantaged half of the population is equivalent to a major aircrash or shipwreck every day (Jacobson *et al.*, 1991).

- There would be 42,000 fewer deaths each year for people aged 16–74, if the death rate of people with manual jobs were the same as for those in non-manual occupations (Jacobson *et al.*, 1991).

- Premature deaths among people with unskilled occupations cause the loss of nearly three times as many years of potential life among men, and twice as many among women, as they do among professionals (Blane *et al.*, 1990).

- The majority of causes of death are more common in manual classes than non-manual: sixty-five out of seventy-eight causes for men and sixty-two out of eighty-two for women (Townsend *et al.*, 1988).

- A child from an unskilled social class is twice as likely to die before the age of 15 as a child with a professional father (Woodroffe *et al.*, 1993).

- If the whole population had experienced the same death rate as the non-manual classes, there would have been 700 fewer stillbirths and 1,500 fewer deaths in the first year of life in England and Wales in 1988 (Delamothe, 1991).

- The prevalence of angina was almost twice as high among middle-aged men in manual occupations, compared with non-manual, in the *British Regional Heart Study* (Pocock *et al.*, 1987).

- Socioeconomic gradients exist for most common causes of long-standing illness and disability – musculoskeletal, heart and circulatory and respiratory conditions – with the highest rates occurring among people in manual occupations (Breeze *et al.*, 1991).

There can be no doubt that such inequalities represent a failure of modern society which can and must be addressed. The main aim of this book is not so much to add to the voluminous literature which has already documented evidence about the nature of the problem, but to begin to make the case that something can and should be done about it. Many of the underlying socioeconomic causes of health inequalities are amenable to changes in public policy. Our objective is to outline a number of practical and affordable ways in which the situation could be dramatically improved if the political will existed to recognise that tackling inequalities in health is a fundamental requirement of social justice for all citizens.

The evidence shows quite convincingly that the more we increase our understanding of the determinants of health, the more inescapable is the conclusion that a person's health cannot be divorced from the social and economic environment in which they live and work. Factors which are increasingly recognised to be of critical importance include:

- the physical environment, such as adequacy of housing, working conditions and air pollution;

- social and economic influences such as income and wealth, levels of unemployment, the quality of the social environment and social support;

- behavioural factors and barriers to adopting a healthier personal lifestyle;
- access to appropriate and effective health and social services.

In this book we advocate the need for new policy initiatives in relation to each of the groups of factors set out above by focusing attention on housing, income maintenance, smoking and access to health care. More generally, we assert that a recognition of the significance of socioeconomic influences has profound implications for promoting the health of the nation through new approaches to prevention. What is required to ensure fairer health outcomes for all is a strategy for formulating, promoting and implementing healthy public policies that transform the nature of social and economic life for those people who are trapped in a web of disadvantage.

The Ditchley Park seminar

It was because of a recognition of the importance of the factors outlined above that the King's Fund responded positively to a suggestion by Sir Donald Acheson, the former Chief Medical Officer for England, that the time was right to consider practical policy options for tackling inequalities in health. As a result, the Fund organised a seminar which was held in September 1993 at Ditchley Park. This book is the result of the presentations and discussions that took place there and subsequent policy analysis during 1994–95.

The aim of the Ditchley Park seminar was to bring together a wide range of people – from central and local government, health authorities and voluntary organisations, to universities and research institutes, professional associations and the media – to try to identify priorities for action in tackling inequalities in health. A selected list of participants who are able and willing to have their names associated with this book is given in the Appendix.

A special effort was made to encourage policy analysts and practitioners from fields other than health to join forces with acknowledged experts in relation to health inequalities. In planning the seminar therefore it was felt to be important to provide an authoritative overview of the nature and extent of health differences between different groups over time. We were fortunate in being able to recruit John Fox, Chief Medical Statistician at the Office of Population Censuses and Surveys, for this purpose. In addition, Margaret Whitehead was commissioned to prepare a comprehensive review of what lessons could be learnt from previous attempts, both in Britain and elsewhere, to improve the health status of people in disadvantaged circumstances. Göran Dahlgren and Louise Gunning-Schepers provided an extremely valuable European dimension, drawing on the experience of their respective countries (Sweden and The Netherlands) which have much stronger political and policy support for action in this area. Raymond Illsley discussed the tradition of research on social inequalities in Britain.

With this material as background information, the Ditchley Park seminar concentrated on four selected areas where new policy initiatives might make a contribution to tackling inequalities in health. We particularly wanted to consider the very important role of social policies outside the health sector. Richard Best agreed to review aspects of housing policy and Richard Berthoud covered issues related to poverty and income maintenance policy, with special reference to families with dependent children. We also thought it was important to examine one of the most significant behavioural factors associated with poor health, and Joy Townsend reviewed issues related to smoking. Finally, although we do not believe that the NHS is the agency principally responsible for reducing health inequalities, we were keen to consider how health authorities could make use of the new freedoms available to them in determining their purchasing priorities, and Chris Ham reviewed possibilities in this area.

Using the information provided by the papers and presenters outlined above, participants at the Ditchley Park seminar were set three tasks. First, to consider what policy options were serious contenders for action in the different areas. Secondly, to formulate some collective view about priorities. Finally, to reflect on the issues that had not been considered in any detail at Ditchley Park because of time and planning constraints, but which it was thought ought to merit close attention in future.

The aim of this book is to reflect the nature and spirit of the discussions that took place at Ditchley Park. However, it is not primarily a record of the proceedings of the seminar. Additional work was undertaken subsequently and not all of the people who made such excellent presentations at Ditchley Park were able to make further commitments of time to enable us to include their contributions in this book. Fortunately, we were able to persuade other people to supplement and/or substitute where necessary, so that health-related reviews of the four main policy areas discussed at Ditchley Park are included here. In addition, we have included a very brief review of those issues that participants at the seminar felt most strongly had been neglected in our planning. Despite these changes, the final product has, in our view, remained constant to the spirit of Ditchley.

Review of contents

In Chapter 2 John Fox and Michaela Benzeval provide an overall perspective on inequalities in health. They show how existing patterns of mortality and morbidity in Britain have changed over the last century and document the nature and extent of contemporary social inequalities. Evidence is presented from a large variety of sources: vital statistics, longitudinal mortality and morbidity datasets, national prevalence surveys and numerous small-scale studies. The chapter also briefly considers the respective merits of the different explanatory models which have been developed in this area of often intense political debate. The authors conclude by arguing that there are substantial variations in health in Britain which reflect individuals' social and economic circumstances.

In Chapter 3 Margaret Whitehead reviews international evidence about policy initiatives that have been introduced to try to tackle inequalities in health. She identifies initiatives at four different levels which may have relevance for Britain:

• strengthening individuals;

• strengthening communities;

• improving access to essential facilities and services;

• encouraging macroeconomic and cultural change.

Working through each level in turn, the chapter reviews the types of interventions that have been introduced to reduce inequalities in health, and provides detailed case studies and examples of some of the better evaluated studies. Finally, it draws together evidence about more strategic approaches to tackling inequalities in health and considers what lessons can be drawn for future policy making from all relevant experiences.

Chapters 4–7 single out four different elements of equity policy for analysis in much greater depth. They ask the question – in relation to housing, income maintenance, smoking and access to health care – what could be tried? These are just four out of the many issues requiring attention and do not constitute a comprehensive review of equity policy. They were selected to illustrate the four main sets of factors that influence the social distribution of health: environmental, social and economic, behavioural and access to health care. They are meant to give a flavour of the huge range of policy initiatives that could approach the task of tackling inequalities in health.

Housing was chosen as an environmental determinant of health, concerned with the physical and social conditions in which people live. In Britain, housing has long been an issue of public health concern and, as we still have some of the coldest, dampest housing stock in Europe, as well as a large homeless population, it could be considered an urgent priority for action today. In Chapter 4 Richard Best, Director of the Joseph Rowntree Foundation, reviews the relationship between housing and health and considers the policy options that might be most appropriate to reduce inequalities in health.

The chapter begins by examining the housing problems facing Britain today: the growth of homelessness, poor housing conditions and inadequate local environments, and reviews how these might result in poor health. Next, the context in which housing policies are implemented is considered: the change in public finance in terms of investment in social housing and financial assistance; and the role of the housing sector in the national economy. Finally, the chapter summarises the policy recommendations in the housing field that are most appropriate to reduce inequalities in health.

Family poverty is perhaps the most important example of social and economic influences on health. Adequate incomes provide the fundamental prerequisites for health: food, shelter, warmth and the ability to participate in society. Unfortunately, many people in Britain do not have access to these. As there are over eleven million people living in or on the margins of poverty in Britain today, it is a pressing problem for anyone concerned with public health. In Chapter 5 therefore Michaela Benzeval, and Steven Webb, from the Institute for Fiscal Studies, review the relationship between low income and health and consider appropriate policy options.

Chapter 5 begins by examining which population groups in Britain experience low income and finds that families with dependent children are over-represented among them. Evidence from Britain and other countries about the association between income and health is then reviewed and the chapter considers the mechanisms by which low income might cause ill health. Next, it reviews a range of policy options which would both tackle the causes of poverty directly and alleviate its consequences. Finally, it examines how the taxation system might be made more progressive in ways which would raise revenue to support some of the other policy recommendations to tackle inequalities in health.

Smoking was selected as an example of an individual behavioural factor frequently targeted for action in national health strategies. It was chosen because smoking is seen as a major cause of preventable mortality and morbidity in its own right, but also because it is increasingly a habit of people living in poverty, leading some to see it as a key contributor to observed social inequalities in health.

In Chapter 6 Joy Townsend, from the Wolfson Institute for Preventive Medicine, begins by examining the social distribution of smoking and establishing that prevalence is much higher among people in disadvantaged circumstances. She then considers the strong relationship between smoking and inequalities in health. Evidence about policies which have been implemented to reduce smoking prevalence is then reviewed, with particular emphasis placed on the impact such policies might have among people with poor socioeconomic circumstances. Such initiatives range from individually focused strategies, such as cessation support, to regulation about advertising and smoking in public places and finally to the contentious debate about tobacco taxation. The chapter concludes by summarising the recommendations felt to be most appropriate to tackle inequalities in health.

Access to health care is the final substantive topic, although there is very little evidence that investment in health services contributes to either the overall level of health status in a country or its social distribution. As other chapters show, it is differences in living standards that primarily influence social variations in health. Nevertheless, the health service has a vital role to play in any strategy to tackle inequalities. First, it should ensure that the services it provides are equitable, by allocating resources according to need. Secondly, it should provide appropriate services in convenient locations to meet the particular needs of people in disadvantaged circumstances. Finally, the Department of Health and local health purchasers must take the lead in encouraging the development of equity-orientated healthy public policies.

Chapter 7 assesses the role of the health service in these important areas. It considers how well current resource allocation mechanisms are related to need and how they might be improved. It then assesses, at a more practical level, whether access to services on the basis of need has been achieved, in terms of overall expenditure, prevention, screening and treatment in primary and secondary care. Next, it advocates that more information about the social distribution of health service use should be collected and that priority should be given to the development of community-based services to improve the access of the most disadvantaged groups. Finally, it considers the wider role of the health service to provide an information and monitoring service, undertake health impact assessments and tackle the socioeconomic determinants of health directly at both the local and the national level.

The four issues chosen for in-depth analysis necessarily represent only part of any agenda for action that would represent a serious attempt to tackle inequalities in health. At the Ditchley Park seminar participants suggested other issues that would form part of a more comprehensive strategy.

A number of areas of unfinished business are outlined in Chapter 8. First, participants were concerned about the over-emphasis in British research on inequalities in health among white men of working age, partly because of the excessive reliance on data about social class. Women, older people and minority ethnic groups are a growing proportion of the British population who experience social and economic disadvantage. We therefore felt it was important to place specific emphasis on these groups. Chapter 8 very briefly highlights evidence which both demonstrates the particular vulnerability of women, older people and minority ethnic groups to social and economic disadvantage and illustrates the consequences for their health. Secondly, participants were concerned that insufficient time was given to a consideration of unemployment, poor education and inadequate childcare facilities. Chapter 8 therefore illustrates how each of these issues is associated with inequalities in health and considers some policy options which have recently been advocated by other groups.

Time for action

The rationale for this book is the belief that there is no room for reasonable doubt that observed social inequalities in health are amenable to purposeful policy interventions. The problem is well documented and the solution becomes clearer every day. What is needed is a determined effort to create a fairer society that embraces all sections of the community.

We cannot pretend that we have considered every possible strategy or that the precise health benefits that might flow from different interventions are clearly understood. What we do claim is that the problem of health inequalities is a real and substantial one which demands urgent attention. In this book we set out a practical *agenda for action* which would do much to improve the situation. What is much more important than the precise policy mix, however, is a real commitment at the highest levels of government to take this issue seriously.

We see this book as a modest first attempt to make out a real case for change. As Trollope's statement of nineteenth century radical Liberal philosophy – quoted at the beginning of this introduction – suggests, it may prove impossible to eradicate inequalities. Nevertheless, it is time that much more concerted efforts were made to lessen the degree to which material and social deprivation reduce the length and the quality of the lives of the poorest sections of British society.

CHAPTER **2**

Perspectives on social variations in health

John Fox and Michaela Benzeval

Introduction

In Britain mortality rates at all ages are two to three times higher among disadvantaged social groups than their more affluent counterparts. Individuals with poor socioeconomic circumstances also experience higher levels of illness and disability. Evidence that such differentials in health exist is found in all countries, based on numerous studies which measure both health and socioeconomic status in a variety of ways. Explanations about the causes, however, are complex. It is likely that a combination of factors is at work reflecting people's living and working conditions, their resources, social relationships and lifestyles.

The purpose of this chapter is to briefly highlight the key pieces of national evidence and explanations. It begins by describing the vast changes in health which have occurred over the last hundred years, against which background current patterns of mortality and morbidity need to be considered. Next, evidence about the extent of variations in Britain today is described, highlighting some of the key sources and findings. Finally, the different explanations that have been put forward and their relative merits are examined.

Background: the changing pattern of health

There has been a substantial reduction in mortality rates in England and Wales throughout the twentieth century. This has been particularly true for infants, children and young adults. Figure 2.1 shows that mortality rates for children aged 1–4 were fifty times higher at the beginning of the century than in the late 1980s. However, mortality rates for over-85s were only 1.5 times greater in 1901–05 than they are today.

Over the same period there have been substantial changes in the main causes of death. At the beginning of the century, infectious and respiratory diseases were the most important. These have now been replaced by more chronic illnesses, which affect mainly middle-aged and older people, such as cancer and cardiovascular diseases (Swerdlow, 1987). Overall this has had a profound impact on life expectancy, such that over half of male babies and 66 per cent of female babies born today can expect to live to be 80 years old.

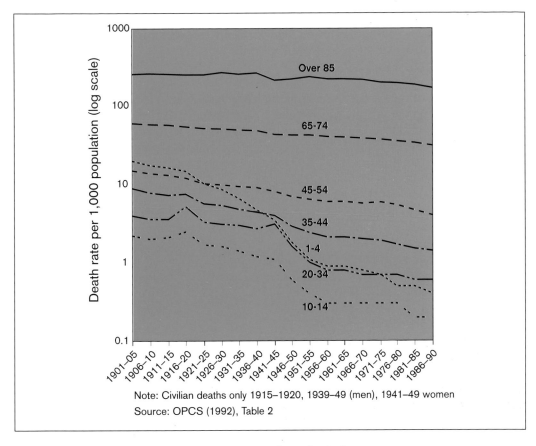

Figure 2.1: Death rate per 1,000 population by selected age groups, England and Wales, 1901–90

These reductions in mortality have dramatically changed the age structure of the population in Britain. In 1901, individuals aged 75 and over accounted for only 1.6 per cent of the population against 13 per cent in 1991. In contrast, children under 5 accounted for 13 per cent of the population in 1901 compared to 7 per cent in 1991. Population changes have resulted in a very different burden of morbidity and mortality from that experienced earlier in the century. In 1911, for example, 30 per cent of male and 26 per cent of female deaths occurred among children under 5. In 1991 deaths in this age group accounted for less than 2 per cent of the total. In contrast, the proportion of total deaths occurring over 85 has risen substantially, from 5 per cent in 1911 to nearly one-third in 1991.

Evidence of social variations in health

Socioeconomic differences in health have been recorded in Britain for more than a century. The earliest work, conducted by Farr (1860), identified the causes of differences in mortality between different localities. He believed that this would enable an assessment to be made about how to improve health by understanding the environmental differences between more and less healthy areas. At the beginning of the twentieth century Stevenson

(1923) grouped together similar occupations into social classes in order to control for environmental factors when examining occupational differences in health. Since then there has been a regular supply of national data which show that the more affluent members of society live longer and enjoy better health than those who are less advantaged.

In the remainder of this section we review the key pieces of British evidence. We consider mortality data from vital statistics and longitudinal surveys as well as morbidity data obtained from national prevalence surveys. For both mortality and morbidity, an association is found with individuals' social and economic circumstances measured by occupation, housing tenure, car ownership, employment status, education and income.

Mortality

The 1970–72 decennial supplement of occupational mortality indicated that on average men in social class V – unskilled occupations – were 2.5 times more likely to die before reaching 65 years of age than their professional counterparts in social class I (OPCS, 1978). Evidence from the most recent decennial supplement (OPCS, 1986a) is shown in Figure 2.2. For children and adults of working age there is a rise in standardised mortality ratios from social class I to V. People in unskilled occupations and their children are twice as likely to die prematurely as professionals.

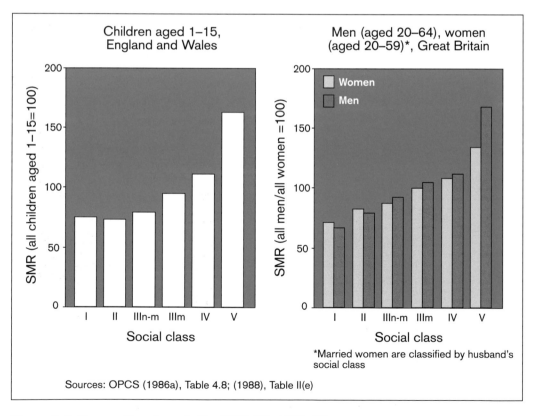

Sources: OPCS (1986a), Table 4.8; (1988), Table II(e)

Figure 2.2: Occupational mortality 1979–80, 1982–83

Analysis of these data by cause of death shows that gradients in mortality by social class are apparent for nearly all causes of death to a greater or lesser extent. However, in infancy, childhood and adulthood (15–64) the steepest gradients are found in deaths from accidents and from infectious and respiratory diseases.

An alternative way of examining the occupational mortality data is to consider the years of potential life lost by different social groups. This gives greater emphasis to deaths that occur at younger ages. Men in social class V lost 114 years of potential life per 1,000 population against 39 years in class I. This reflects the particularly high mortality rates due to accidents and violence among young men in social class V. For women the figures were much lower, with those in unskilled occupations losing 34 years and professionals 16 (Blane *et al.*, 1990).

Evidence of variations in mortality has been strengthened in the 1980s as a result of the publication of findings from a number of different longitudinal datasets. Such studies have considerably increased understanding of the differences observed. The most substantial longitudinal dataset was begun in 1971 and links all vital registration information to the census records of 1 per cent of the population of England and Wales (Goldblatt, 1990a). The *Longitudinal Study* (LS) has enabled researchers to overcome many of the criticisms of analyses based on the decennial supplements. In addition to confirming the differences in mortality for men of working age, the LS has provided a more detailed examination of mortality among women (discussed below) and among older people. Figure 2.3 shows

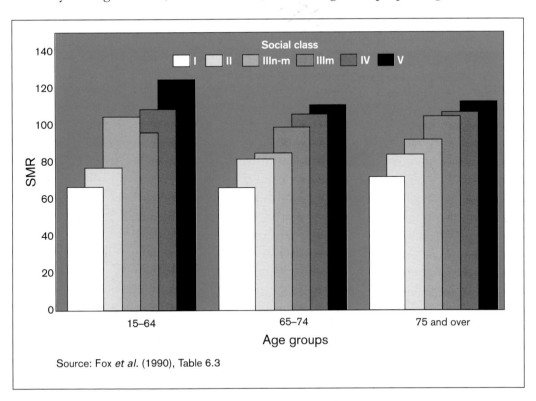

Source: Fox *et al.* (1990), Table 6.3

Figure 2.3: Mortality of men by social class and broad age groups,
***Longitudinal Study,* England and Wales, 1976–81**

male mortality among the LS participants by social class and age between 1976 and 1981. For each age group there is a steep upward gradient in SMRs from social class I to V. The gradient becomes shallower as age increases. However, men over 75 in social class V still have a more than 50 per cent higher death rate than those in social class I (Fox *et al.*, 1990).

The LS has also demonstrated the value of other measures of social and economic circumstances, such as housing tenure and car ownership. These have been found to be 'more effective discriminators of mortality differences than social class' (Goldblatt, 1990b, p. 171) and overcome the problems of being unable to analyse women as a group using social class (Moser *et al.*, 1990a). For example, as Figure 2.4 shows, between 1976 and 1981 women and men in owner-occupied accommodation with access to a car had an SMR of 78 against that of 138 for women and 129 for men in local authority rented accommodation without a car. This evidence is particularly important because it demonstrates that a strong socioeconomic gradient exists for women as well as for men.

The LS also includes information about cancer registration and mortality. Analysis of these data by a variety of socioeconomic measures shows significantly higher registration rates among people in disadvantaged circumstances for cancer of the cervix, stomach and lung. However, breast and ovarian cancers are more prevalent among more affluent sections of the population (Leon, 1988). Although most of the socioeconomic mortality differences reflect such differences in incidence, there is some evidence that manual social classes are more likely to die once the disease has been diagnosed (Kogevinas, 1990).

Other longitudinal datasets have also demonstrated the existence of social gradients in mortality. The *Whitehall Study*, begun in 1967, has followed the health of 17,000 male civil servants.

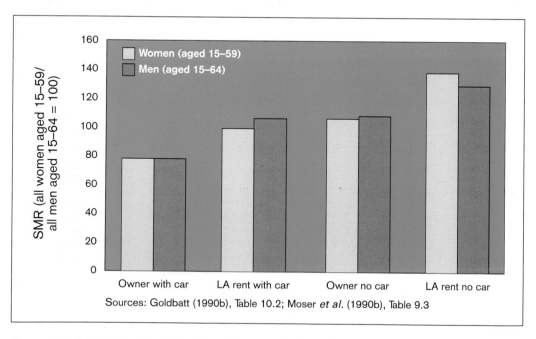

Figure 2.4: Mortality of adults of working age by housing tenure and access to car, *Longitudinal Study,* England and Wales, 1976–81

Analysing subsequent mortality by employment grade, Marmot and colleagues (1984) found that men in the lowest grades were three times more likely to die than those in the highest.

Morbidity

Most of the early studies of socioeconomic differences in health had to rely solely on mortality data. However, in recent years a number of rich national datasets have been made available that allow individuals' morbidity experiences to be linked to their social and economic circumstances.

A regular national source of information on morbidity is the *General Household Survey* (GHS). This includes information on approximately 25,000 people each year in Great Britain. A number of analyses have shown social gradients – measured by socioeconomic group, housing tenure, car ownership and employment status – in self-reported health status. For example, age-standardised morbidity ratios for chronic illness are approximately 40 per cent higher for people in local authority accommodation without a car than for owner occupiers with two or more cars (Haynes, 1991). Age-standardised limiting long-standing illness rates for people who are unemployed are over 70 per cent higher than those of individuals who are employed (Arber, 1991).

In 1985–86 a national *Health and Lifestyle Survey* of 9,000 people included both self-assessed measures of health and more objective measurements such as lung function, blood pressure and cognitive tests. A number of analyses of the survey have demonstrated that a whole range of different health indicators are associated with a variety of measures of individuals' social and economic circumstances (Cox *et al.*, 1987; Blaxter, 1990; Benzeval *et al.*, 1992). For example, as Figure 2.5 shows, twice as many men and women aged 40–65 in social classes

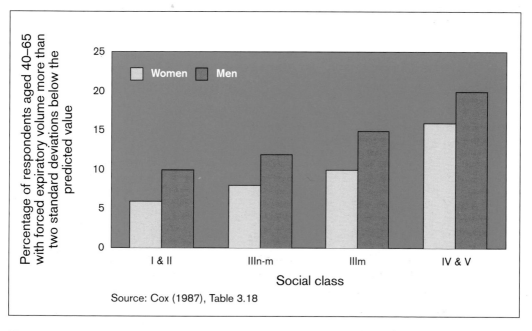

Source: Cox (1987), Table 3.18

Figure 2.5: Inadequate respiratory function and social class, respondents aged 40–65, *Health and Lifestyle Survey,* **Great Britain, 1985–86**

IV and V were classified as having only poor or fair lung function, based on nurse measurement of forced expiratory volume, as respondents in classes I or II (Cox, 1987).

The recent *Health Survey for England* (White *et al.*, 1993) showed that a range of factors such as height, blood pressure, body mass index and cardiovascular disorder vary with social class. For example, as can be seen in Figure 2.6, a measure of hypertension – having a diastolic blood pressure greater than 95 mmHg – is more prevalent among manual social classes.

Morbidity resulting in doctor consultations can also be shown to vary between social and economic groups. For example, data taken from the fourth study of *Morbidity Statistics from General Practice* show that age-standardised consultation rates for serious conditions are significantly higher among local authority tenants, people who are unemployed and people born in the Caribbean or the Indian subcontinent than in the general population (McCormick *et al.*, 1995).

A host of other national surveys have also demonstrated socioeconomic differences for a large number of health indicators. These include the *OPCS Omnibus Survey* (Benzeval *et al.*, 1994); the *National Child Development Study* (Power *et al.*, 1991); and *The Dietary and Nutritional Survey of British Adults* (Gregory *et al.*, 1990).

Overview

The previous section highlights some of the findings that demonstrate socioeconomic differences in health. The key point to emphasise is that across a range of dimensions of health – mortality, medically diagnosed morbidity, self-assessed objective and subjective health measurements – there is evidence of variations, whether measured by social class,

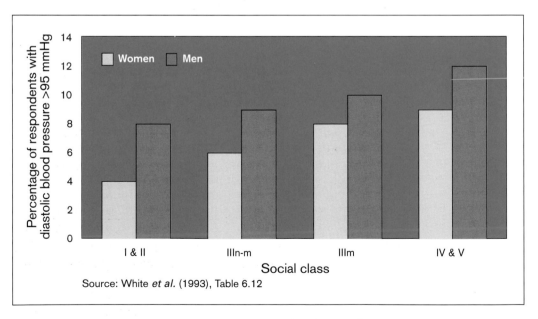

Source: White *et al.* (1993), Table 6.12

Figure 2.6: Hypertension and social class, *Health Survey for England,* 1991

housing tenure, income, car ownership, economic status or education. Such differences exist at all ages, from birth to beyond retirement, and have been found in a wide range of datasets, including official statistics, cross-sectional and longitudinal surveys and numerous small-scale studies. Given the extent of the evidence, the existence of substantial differences in health can be in no doubt.

But what does this mean? At its most fundamental, people in the least privileged circumstances can expect to live eight years less than the most privileged.

> *Furthermore, if all infants and children up to age 15 enjoyed the same survival chances as the children from classes I and II, then over 3,000 deaths a year might be prevented. . . . In addition, bringing all adults aged 16–64 up to the mortality experience of class I would mean 39,000 fewer deaths per year.*
>
> (Whitehead, 1992, p. 229)

Explanations

The conventional starting point for a discussion of different explanations is the Black Report (Townsend and Davidson, 1982), which suggested that the four main possibilities were that social variations in health are:

- an artefact of measurement error;
- the product of social selection;
- caused by individuals' behaviours;
- a result of individuals' material and social circumstances.

There have been a number of comprehensive reviews of this framework of explanations (see, for example, Blane, 1985; Macintyre, 1986; Whitehead, 1992; Davey Smith *et al.*, 1994). Below we briefly highlight the key arguments and evidence about their relative importance.

Artefact

It has been proposed that the differences in mortality by social class reported in the Black Report are an artefact of the way the statistics are derived. Proponents of this argument (Illsley, 1986) suggest that there are a number of reasons for this, including numerator/denominator bias and the unstable meaning of social class over time.

Systematic biases may occur in the decennial supplement of occupational mortality because the numerator and denominator are derived from different sources. However, equally strong socioeconomic gradients in mortality and morbidity have been found in both longitudinal and cross-sectional studies where all data are collected from the same source. Similarly, although there are problems with the use of social class, particularly over time, numerous other measures of socioeconomic status have demonstrated similar patterns. No dataset will ever be perfect, but the size and consistency of evidence suggest that the artefact explanation can be largely discounted.

Social selection

Social selection occurs when social variations in health arise as a result of social mobility. Healthy individuals tend to be promoted, whereas those in poor health find it difficult to obtain employment or have to take less demanding jobs. In this way health determines social position rather than social circumstances determining health status. Illsley (1955) identified this phenomenon by demonstrating that taller women tended to marry into social classes higher than their fathers' more often than shorter women did. The infant mortality rates and the birthweight of their babies were then better than those of their peers who remained in their original social class.

More recent evidence, however, suggests that although social mobility may indeed be health related, the differences in mortality observed among men towards the end of working age and beyond retirement age are strong testimony against the social selection theory (Fox *et al.*, 1990). Overall, although there is some evidence of social selection at younger ages, it is only likely to account for a small proportion of the mortality differential between social groups (Whitehead, 1992).

Behaviour

The behaviourist explanation suggests that people in disadvantaged circumstances experience poor health because they are more likely to participate in health-damaging behaviour such as smoking. Chapter 6 shows that there is a clear gradient in smoking by socioeconomic status, with smoking rates highest among the most disadvantaged social groups. There can be little argument that such behaviour is reflected in poor health outcomes. However, there are a number of studies which show that, having controlled for behaviour, social gradients in health still exist. For example, in the *Whitehall Study* there was a strong gradient by employment grade for coronary heart disease among non-smokers (Marmot *et al.*, 1984). Similarly, a prospective study in Alameda County in the USA, which controlled for behavioural factors such as smoking, drinking and exercise, reported that the poorest groups had death rates 1.5 times those of the richest (Haan *et al.*, 1987).

More importantly, it must be remembered that 'these behaviours plainly are embedded in the social structure. When questions are asked not merely how people behave but why they behave as they do, "lifestyles" provide no release from the need to confront that structure' (Morris, 1990, p. 492). This point can be illustrated with two different examples.

First, there is considerable variation among social groups regarding the extent of choice they have over their behaviours. For example, smoking may be chosen by women as a coping strategy, enabling them to look after their families in difficult circumstances, despite its adverse health consequences (Graham, 1993a). Blaxter's recognition of this phenomenon led her to conclude that 'there is no doubt that behaviour is implicated, but it is behaviour which is inevitable in certain environments' (1983, p. 1142).

Secondly, the social distribution of smoking has changed substantially since the Second World War. It has been suggested that this is because messages about the harmful effects of smoking have been promoted through educational media to which people in more affluent circumstances have been more receptive (Hart, 1986). It is at least conceivable that the policy instrument chosen to reduce smoking might be responsible for exacerbating the social differences in smoking observed in the 1990s. For example, if more emphasis had been placed on taxation policies rather than health education to reduce the prevalence of smoking, the resulting change in social distribution might have been rather different.

Interpretations such as these have led many commentators to argue that 'the distinction between cultural/behavioural and materialist explanations is artificial' (Blane, 1985, p. 434). 'They probably interact and it may be more helpful to find the right balance between them rather than viewing them as mutually exclusive' (Macintyre, 1986, p. 405).

Material and social circumstances

In addition to their indirect influence through health-damaging behaviour, material and social circumstances have a direct impact on individuals' health status.

Material circumstances

There has been a plethora of studies that have demonstrated the association between poor material and physical environments and high levels of mortality and morbidity. A number of comprehensive reviews of the latest evidence on material deprivation and health can be found in BMA (1987), Blackburn (1991) and Whitehead (1992).

At an ecological level, a number of studies have found very strong associations between census-based measures of deprivation and health. Using the 1981 census at ward level in the northern region, Townsend and colleagues (1988) found strong and statistically significant positive correlations between measures of deprivation – the proportion of the population in wards who were unemployed; living in overcrowded accommodation; without access to a car; not owner occupiers; or in manual classes – and various health indicators – SMR under 65; low birthweight babies; and the level of permanent sickness. For example, the SMR for under-65s in the most deprived 10 per cent of wards was 1.73 times higher than that in the least deprived decile. Repeating this analysis with the 1991 census, the ratio of mortality rates had increased to 1.95 (Phillimore *et al.*, 1994). Similar analyses have been conducted for wards within all health regions in England (Eames *et al.*, 1993) and postcode sectors in Scotland (Carstairs and Morris, 1991). In both studies strong statistical correlations were found between various measures of deprivation and mortality.

More specifically, Robinson and Pinch suggest a range of factors implicated in childhood, including:

> *damp housing leading to increased amounts of respiratory infection; household over-crowding facilitating the spread of infection; inadequate diet associated with low incomes ... failure to perceive the seriousness of childhood illness by poorly educated and informed parents; stresses leading to child abuse; a generally poor environment increasing the risks of child accidents; together with the everyday strain of coping with a demanding young family in inadequate circumstances in areas suffering from multiple deprivation.*

> (1987, p. 14)

19

Evidence from the LS demonstrates that men who are unemployed and their wives have significantly raised mortality after controlling for other socioeconomic factors (Moser *et al.*, 1990c). Elsewhere in this book, Webb and Benzeval show that individuals with low incomes report more ill health than their more affluent counterparts. In Chapter 4, Best highlights how homelessness, damp housing, poor housing design and deprived neighbourhoods can all have a detrimental impact on health. Chapter 7 shows how individuals in disadvantaged circumstances may have inadequate access to health services, either because resources are not allocated in relation to need or because of economic, geographic or cultural barriers. All of these factors may exacerbate inequalities in health.

In addition to evidence about the association between individuals' current circumstances and their health experience there is growing support for the notion that poor conditions in early life are associated with premature mortality in adulthood. For example, Barker and colleagues (1993) have suggested that 'low growth rates *in utero* and during infancy are associated with high death rates from cardiovascular disease' (p. 938). They argue that the main cause of such poor growth rates is undernutrition of mothers during pregnancy due to deprivation. However, given the strong association between deprivation in childhood and later life, it is difficult to untangle which is more important for adult mortality (Ben-Shlomo and Davey Smith, 1991).

Social circumstances

Poor social circumstances are increasingly recognised as an important cause of ill health. However, the role of social factors in determining health has been less thoroughly investigated than other causes. Nevertheless, there is a growing body of evidence which suggests that factors such as social support, integration and isolation, and social networks and roles are also associated with health. For example, Marmot and Theorell (1988) explored the relationship between psychosocial working conditions – skill discretion, authority over decisions and social support at work – and health, and found that men working in conditions classified as 'non-learning' or 'monotonous' were more likely to die from cardiovascular diseases than others, even after adjusting for social class. More generally, using data on individuals' social relationships from the *Health and Lifestyle Survey*, Blaxter (1990) found that high age-standardised morbidity ratios for both physical and psychosocial health were associated with low levels of social integration and support.

Overview

The causes of the variations described in this chapter are complex and multiple. Social selection probably plays a minor role, whereas individuals' resources and social relationships, and their behaviour, are the most important. Blaxter (1990) suggests that ' "circumstances" – not only socioeconomic circumstances and the external environment, but also the individual's psychosocial environment – carry rather more weight, as determinants of health, than healthy or unhealthy behaviours' (p. 233).

Conclusion

The purpose of this chapter has not been to explain the precise causes of social and economic variations in health but to highlight their continued existence and to identify the range of factors that might be implicated. It is clear that health is strongly associated with the social and economic environment in which people live. Changing population and employment structures, and falls in mortality and morbidity at younger ages, mean that there is a growing social, economic and political importance attached to differences in health among women and among older people (see Figure 8.1, p. 126). This knowledge offers opportunities to secure gains in the health of the population through policies designed both to change the social and economic environment and to improve the health of particular sub-groups of the population.

CHAPTER **3**

Tackling inequalities: a review of policy initiatives

Margaret Whitehead

Given the overwhelming case for taking action to tackle social inequalities in health, the purpose of this chapter is to review initiatives that have already been taken. The key question to be addressed is: what policies have helped or hindered the goal of reducing such inequalities? In an attempt to answer this question, initiatives taken at four distinct policy levels are reviewed, before looking at more strategic approaches that have spanned several. Conclusions to inform future action are then drawn.

First, a framework is needed for considering the various possibilities for action and how they might contribute to the larger goal of tackling inequalities in health. The starting point chosen here is the determinants of health in general and inequalities in health in particular.

Factors influencing health

It is now accepted that there are many influences on an individual's health, often categorised into biological factors; the physical and social environment; personal lifestyle; and health services. However, when considering policy options it can be useful to think in terms of layers of influence, one on top of the other, as illustrated in Figure 3.1 (Dahlgren and Whitehead, 1991). At the centre are individuals, endowed with age, sex and genetic factors that undoubtedly influence their final health potential, but which could be considered as fixed and therefore appear as part of the core in the figure. Surrounding the individuals are layers of influences on health that theoretically could be modified. The innermost layer represents the personal behaviour and way of life that individuals adopt and that have been shown to have health-damaging or health-promoting potential. But individuals do not exist in a vacuum: they interact with friends, relatives and the immediate community around them, and come under the social and community influences represented in the next layer. Mutual support within a community can sustain the health

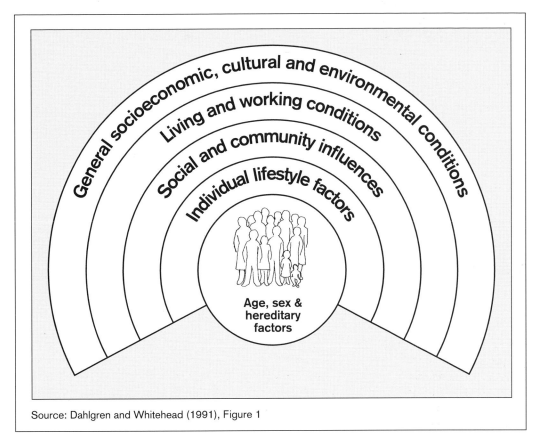

Source: Dahlgren and Whitehead (1991), Figure 1

Figure 3.1: The main determinants of health

of its members in otherwise unfavourable conditions. Without this support, social isolation can set in and adversely affect people's health. These social interactions and peer pressures can also influence personal behaviours in the layer below, for better or worse. Then there are the wider influences on a person's ability to maintain health, represented in layer 3 – factors in their immediate surroundings encountered as part of their daily life – their living and working conditions, food supplies and access to essential facilities and services.

Overall, there are the economic, cultural and environmental conditions prevalent in society as a whole, represented in layer 4. Clearly, factors in this layer, such as the economic state of a country and labour market conditions, have a bearing on every other layer. The standard of living achieved in a society, for example, can influence an individual's choice of housing, work and social interactions, as well as eating and drinking habits, smoking and exercise. Cultural beliefs about, for example, the place of women in society, or pervasive attitudes to minority ethnic communities, can influence their standard of living and socioeconomic position. Whereas some environmental pollution factors are governed by living and working conditions (layer 3), others are the result of wider structural factors represented in layer 4. For example, how much industrial pollution a country is prepared to tolerate is influenced by attitudes to economic growth.

It is the range and inter-relationship of all the different determinants of health that Figure 3.1 seeks to stress. If one health hazard or risk factor is focused upon, it is important to examine how it fits in with the other layers of influence, and whether it could be considered a primary cause or merely a symptom of a larger problem represented in some other layer.

Most influences on health demonstrate a social gradient, with conditions conducive to health becoming less favourable with declining social status. There is therefore an uneven distribution of health hazards and risk factors across the population, resulting in groups with lower status, power or income carrying a heavier burden of ill health. So, for example, in relation to layer 1 there tends to be a higher prevalence of behavioural factors such as smoking and poor diet among people in disadvantaged circumstances, but also greater financial barriers to choosing a healthier personal lifestyle. From layer 2, indicators of community organisation register fewer networks and support systems available to people towards the lower end of the social scale, compounded by the conditions prevalent in areas of high deprivation, which have fewer social services and amenities for community activity, weaker security arrangements and inconvenient, even hazardous, layouts for children and older people, encouraging isolation and loneliness still further.

In relation to layer 3, poorer housing conditions, exposure to more dangerous or stressful working conditions and evidence of poorer access to health, welfare and education services indicate a differential risk across the population. People living in poverty have greatly reduced chances of securing such basic prerequisites for health. Finally, in relation to layer 4 there is evidence of a differential impact of economic and labour market policies on different sections of the population. Such policies can lead to vast differences in the standard of living enjoyed by different groups in society.

In thinking about a policy response, questions need to be asked about the size of the contribution each of the four layers and their constituent factors make to the health divide; the feasibility of changing specific factors; and the complementary action that would be required to influence linked factors in other layers.

Policy responses

Recent searches of the medical and health literature for evaluated interventions tackling inequalities in health have been carried out for the Dutch government (Gepkens and Gunning-Schepers, 1993) and for the Northern Regional Health Authority (Bunton *et al.*, 1994). In addition, for the World Health Organization (WHO) a review of initiatives, extending to a wider policy field beyond the health literature, is continuing (Whitehead and Dahlgren, 1991; Dahlgren and Whitehead, 1992; Dahlgren, 1993). The responses revealed by these reviews tend to fall into one of four main policy levels:

- strengthening individuals;

- strengthening communities;

- improving access to essential facilities and services;

- encouraging macroeconomic and cultural change.

Each policy level has a distinct aim, ranging from strengthening individuals, through strengthening communities, to the practical public health measures that improve living and working conditions, and finally to macroeconomic changes influencing the standard of living achieved in a society. A brief description of each of these is given below. Subsequently, evidence about the impact of interventions in each area is reviewed more extensively.

At the first level, policy responses are aimed at strengthening individuals in disadvantaged circumstances, employing person-based strategies. These policies are based on the premise that building up a person's knowledge, motivation, competence or skills will enable them to alter their behaviour in relation to personal risk factors, or to cope better with the stresses and strains imposed by external health hazards from other layers of influence.

Examples of strategies employed at this policy level include stress management education for people working in monotonous conditions, counselling services for people who become unemployed to help prevent the associated decline in mental health, and supportive smoking cessation clinics for women with low incomes. Sometimes these policies may be expected to have a direct impact on inequalities in health, for example if they were successful in reducing smoking rates among people in poor socioeconomic circumstances. But often the potential effect would be more indirect – counselling services for people who are unemployed are not going to reduce the unemployment rate, but may ameliorate the worst health effects of unemployment and prevent further damage.

The second policy level is concerned with strengthening communities. This is focused on how people in disadvantaged communities can join together for mutual support and in so doing strengthen the whole community's defence against health hazards. The community development strategies at this level recognise the intrinsic strengths that families, friends, voluntary organisations and communities can have, over and above the capabilities of individuals working in isolation. For example, Wallace (1993) identifies several critical functions that strong social networks within a distinct geographic neighbourhood can serve to create healthier conditions for a poor community, including:

- social control of illegal activity and of substance abuse;

- socialisation of the young as participating members of a community;

- limiting duration and intensity of youthful 'experimentation' with dangerous and destructive activity;

- providing first employment;

- improving access to formal and informal health care;

- social support for health maintenance;

- allowing the exercise of political power to direct resources to that community and to deflect threats.

These policies recognise the importance to society of social cohesion, as well as the need to create the conditions in deprived neighbourhoods for community dynamics to work.

The third policy level focuses on improving access to essential facilities and services. These policies tackle the physical and psychosocial conditions in which people live and work, ensuring better access to what WHO calls 'the prerequisites for health' – including clean water, sanitation, adequate housing, safe and fulfilling employment, safe and nutritious food supplies, essential health care, educational services and welfare in times of need. Such policies are normally the responsibility of separate sectors, often operating independently of each other but with the potential for co-operation.

The fourth and final policy level is aimed at encouraging macroeconomic or cultural changes to reduce poverty and the wider adverse effects of inequality on society. These include macroeconomic and labour market policies, the encouragement of cultural values promoting equal opportunities and environmental hazard control on a national and international scale. What these policies have in common is that they tend to span several sectors and work across the population as a whole, unlike the ones in levels 1 and 2 that focus on the most disadvantaged individuals, groups and areas. However, they can have a differential impact on the standard of living and opportunities open to different groups in the population, and as such have the potential to reduce inequalities.

Within this framework attention will be focused on three key questions.

- What determinants of the health divide are being addressed?

- Is the aim to tackle a determinant of health directly, or to ameliorate the health effects indirectly?

- What are the aims of the strategies employed, and what is known of the effectiveness/ adequacy of such strategies?

A major problem in attempting to address such questions is the fact that policies, particularly major structural ones, are rarely introduced for health reasons, let alone with the aim of reducing inequalities in health, and so they have not been monitored for health outcomes. Furthermore, only in exceptional circumstances have policies been introduced experimentally, to provide the opportunity to compare control and intervention effects. The effect of numerous variables, all operating at the same time, has somehow to be taken into account. For these reasons a broad approach is adopted here, drawing not only on evaluated interventions reported in the literature but also on comparisons over time and between countries when different policies have been in operation.

Strengthening individuals

Many initiatives, particularly those reported in the health literature, have had as a main focus the strengthening of individuals. The aim has been to make up perceived deficiencies in knowledge, practical competence or stress management among people experiencing disadvantage, and to encourage the acquisition of personal or social skills to change their way of life or to be more resilient in the face of adversity. These policies see the problem they seek to address mainly in terms of an individual's personal characteristics and the solution in terms of personal education and development. In what follows the results of initiatives aimed at changing personal behaviour patterns are considered separately from those with an empowerment focus. But first it is worth emphasising that, of the evaluated

Table 3.1: Tackling inequalities in health: type and effectiveness of evaluated interventions reported in the health literature

Type of intervention	Effective	Inconclusive	Ineffective	Total
Structural measures (mainly health care finance)	11	4	1	16
Traditional health care (preventive and screening services)	5	3	3	11
Health education:				
• providing information	6	6	4	16
• providing information and personal support	32	12	5	49
• health promotion and structural measures	2	1	–	3
Remainder	2	1	–	3
Total	**58**	**27**	**13**	**98**

Source: Adapted from Gepkens and Gunning-Schepers (1993), Figure 4

initiatives to tackle inequalities in health, there is an overwhelming concentration at policy level 1.

This can be seen clearly from a review carried out for the Dutch government. Gepkens and Gunning-Schepers (1993) documented ninety-eight evaluated studies aimed at tackling some aspect of inequalities in health, as summarised in Table 3.1. This shows the total number of studies found by type of intervention, with an assessment of how many were effective at meeting their specific aims. Of these, sixty-eight involved personal health education, most tackling behavioural factors. The remainder were almost entirely concerned with a specific aspect of policy level 3 – improving access or uptake in relation to health care. Thus there were sixteen studies mainly related to improving financial access to health care, and eleven aiming to improve uptake of preventive and screening services.

Nevertheless, even though most of these initiatives had a very limited focus, one of the main conclusions of the Dutch review was that there were many more effective studies than expected. For example, forty of the sixty-eight studies in the health education category were effective either in increasing knowledge, changing attitudes or behaviour, or, more rarely, directly improving health outcomes in poorer social and economic groups. Similarly, eleven out of the sixteen initiatives to improve financial access to health care were judged to be effective, as were five of the eleven initiatives to improve preventive and screening services for disadvantaged social groups (Gepkens and Gunning-Schepers, 1993).

Studies with a behavioural focus

Interventions aimed at changing specific behavioural factors have shown mixed results. Those based on providing information in a standard form to the population as a whole have tended to have the greatest impact on advantaged rather than disadvantaged social and economic groups. Some, however, have shown that behavioural change can be encouraged in more disadvantaged groups by a combination of education at the individual level, which takes the need for information, understanding and skills into account, and action at other policy levels to support change, although the process is still slow (Whitehead, 1989; Jacobson *et al.*, 1991).

Perhaps the best example of the impact of information provision on health inequalities is in relation to smoking, where large proportions of the population in many developed countries have been persuaded to give up cigarettes. It has been calculated that, in the absence of the combined efforts of the anti-smoking lobby in the USA, adult per capita cigarette consumption in 1987 would have been at least 80 per cent higher than the actual level (Warner, 1989). However, there has been a differential response, with a less pronounced cessation rate among adult smokers from disadvantaged social groups, particularly in the lowest-income quarter of the population (Marsh and McKay, 1994). The same is true for smoking prevention programmes for children and young people in schools. In the USA and the UK the more comprehensive programmes have consistently shown modest but positive effects, particularly in delaying the onset of tobacco use, but have been less successful in influencing young people from high-risk and minority groups (Glynn, 1989).

Not only do more disadvantaged groups have a higher prevalence of smoking, but they also tend to have a poorer diet, less exercise in leisure time, earlier and more unplanned pregnancies and lower uptake of preventive health care. This social gradient is sometimes attributed to differential knowledge of the facts, or greater fecklessness and irresponsibility among more disadvantaged groups about their own health and that of their families. Yet the evidence accumulating over recent years does not support this proposition. To give just one example, a study in Oxford found that demand for advice about health was widespread and not just confined to people from the middle classes. The association between behavioural factors and health was well recognised by all social groups, and in all social classes a substantial proportion of overweight people wanted to lose weight, smokers wanted to stop and sedentary people wanted to increase exercise. There was no evidence of differential ignorance or unwillingness to contemplate behavioural changes (Coulter, 1987).

On the other hand, what a growing number of studies have shown is that people living and working in disadvantaged circumstances face greater pressures working against change. For example, families living on low income are limited by practical constraints of time, space and money (Burghes, 1980; Lang *et al.*, 1984; Graham, 1986). Social security benefits in Britain have been shown to be too low to meet the necessities of life, such as food, housing and clothing, especially for families with children (Bradshaw *et al.*, 1992). Women living in inadequate housing with heavy family responsibilities experience enormous struggles to keep their families safe and well (Conway, 1993). The effort required to make positive behaviour changes and to avoid health-damaging substances under such conditions is daunting. The use of substances such as tobacco may even be increased at times of greatest environmental and social stress, as a means of coping with what might be perceived as even greater threats to health in the short term (Graham, 1993b).

Taking these findings into consideration, some initiatives have been designed that are sensitive to these very restricting circumstances and are part of broader supporting policies, and some of these show effectiveness in promoting behavioural change among disadvantaged social and economic groups.

A sizeable proportion of interventions at this level have been concerned with maternal and child health, employing midwives, health visitors and other community health workers. These have included studies to improve child accident prevention, breastfeeding prevalence and antenatal preparation, nutrition of pregnant women and babies, and to reduce smoking in pregnancy among disadvantaged populations. Most work on tackling behavioural risk factors in adults with poor socioeconomic status has been concerned with smoking and other cardiovascular disease risks, particularly among black and Hispanic Americans.

Examples of effective initiatives include several schemes combining practical advice and training with safety equipment loans, which have proved effective in encouraging parents with low incomes to increase child safety measures (Colver et al., 1982; Liberato et al., 1989; Robitaille et al., 1990).

A controlled study of education with black women living on low incomes in Chicago showed that breastfeeding rates were increased from 22 per cent in controls to 46 per cent with group classes and 53 per cent with individual counselling by health professionals (Kistin et al., 1990). A breastfeeding initiative in France, using a combination of maternal and professional education with practical support after delivery, recorded a significant increase in the number of women breastfeeding at one month and reduced related physical and medical problems. The greatest benefit was seen among the poorest social class and the women with less formal education (Macquart-Moulin et al., 1990).

In ten randomised trials of preventing smoking in pregnancy, only very limited effect was gained by providing information on the dangers of smoking and firm advice to stop (Lumley and Astbury, 1989), while the most effective interventions emphasised how to give up smoking and developed behavioural strategies tailored to the pregnant smoker (Nowicki et al., 1984; Sexton and Hebel, 1984; Windsor et al., 1985). Two studies were specifically designed to test the response of women on low incomes attending public health care clinics in the USA. One of these achieved a 14 per cent cessation rate with the intervention group compared with 2 per cent in the control group (Windsor et al., 1985). The other achieved an 11 per cent cessation rate with a multiple component programme versus 3 per cent for controls (Mayer et al., 1990). Trials with private patients with high incomes have achieved cessation rates of 27 per cent compared with 3 per cent for controls (Sexton and Hebel, 1984).

Trials like these show that positive changes in behaviour can be achieved with people experiencing disadvantage, even if gains are not always as great as for more advantaged groups. However, there is some evidence that although uptake of health education classes, such as antenatal sessions, tends to be lower among working-class women, for those who do take up the service the classes may have a more powerful influence than for middle-class women. The childbirth classes in one study, for example, had a greater influence on working-class women's attitudes to pain relief, arrangements for the delivery and intention to breastfeed than on middle-class women, who tended to form their opinions and intentions from a wider range of educational sources (Nelson, 1982).

In the food and nutrition field, various attempts have been made to combine nutritional advice to pregnant women on low incomes with supplementation of their diet, in an effort to influence the birthweight of their babies. Favourable, if modest, results have been obtained with balanced carbohydrate/protein supplementation coupled with counselling and other services. Increments of between 30 and 50 grams in mean birthweight have been achieved with such programmes (Rush, 1989). Effects on mortality and morbidity are less certain. However, the results of one such programme in the USA (outlined in Box 3.1) are of particular relevance to a discussion of inequalities in health as they suggest that the largest impact was achieved among black women and those who were less well educated. That is, the intervention was more effective among some of the groups with the highest risk of adverse pregnancy outcomes (Rush *et al.,* 1988a; b; c).

Box 3.1: Nutrition of women and children living on low incomes

The special supplemental food program for women, infants and children was initiated in 1973 in the United States to improve the nutrition of women and children experiencing poverty who have at least one nutritional risk factor. Pregnant or breastfeeding women and children up to age 5 are covered by the scheme, which combines nutritional education with a substantial range of food, from dairy products to fruit juices, and the offer of relevant health services. Coverage of the scheme has grown over the years, so that by the mid-1980s it served over three million people at a cost of $1.56 billion. A national evaluation of the programme was carried out from 1980–85 and found statistically significant positive correlations between the intensity of the service and:

- early registration for antenatal care;
- more frequent antenatal visits;
- duration of gestation;
- mean birthweight;
- reduction in late fetal death.

Improvements in the diets of pregnant women with low incomes were also recorded, but a noted reduction in neonatal death rate was not statistically significant. Analysis of the results by ethnicity and education suggested that the benefits of the programme in terms of reducing late fetal death rates were more pronounced in black women and those with less formal education. In addition, the children who benefited most were those who were small in stature, poor, black and those from lone-parent families.

Sources: Rush *et al.* (1988 a; b; c); Rush (1989)

Other effective interventions focused on cardiovascular disease prevention have employed intensive dietary education over several sessions to produce positive shifts in food selection and eating habits in Americans with low incomes (Bush *et al.*, 1989; Baronowski *et al.*, 1990; Ammerman *et al.*, 1992).

In Britain a reduction in the prevalence of iron deficiency in young children attending an inner-city general practice followed antenatal and postnatal dietary education for mothers coupled with a screening service offered during routine immunisation attendances (James *et al.*, 1989). Experiments with different general practice approaches to smoking education have shown a greater impact among adults from manual social classes when practical demonstrations of the effects of smoking on the lungs were used (Jamrozik *et al.*, 1984).

Studies with an empowerment focus

Some interventions have had a much broader set of aims than altering specific behavioural risk factors, although they are still basically focused on strengthening individuals in one way or another. Several have tried to build up self-confidence and skills in people who are in danger of being swamped by the disadvantaged circumstances in which they live, so that they stand a better chance of maintaining their health and wellbeing whatever external health hazards they encounter. Included in this category are stress management services, social support and counselling to maintain mental health under difficult conditions. Other studies have used empowerment as a tool for helping people who are disadvantaged to gain their rights and better access to the essential facilities and services which could help them to improve their health.

There is now a considerable body of experience in strengthening social support for individuals in disadvantaged circumstances, provided either by statutory and voluntary sources outside the family or by the stimulation of networks from within communities. Some of the more sensitive health advocate and linkworker schemes have also proved their worth to minority ethnic communities by bringing about local service changes as well as providing emotional support (Rocheron and Dickinson, 1990; Parsons and Day, 1992).

It has been suggested that systematic social support, by reducing maternal stress and increasing self-esteem, might not only improve the mental and emotional wellbeing of pregnant women but also increase birthweight, particularly in women from disadvantaged environments, who are at greater risk of stressful life events and lacking in such support. Several controlled trials have been constructed to test these hypotheses, employing regular home visits by specially trained nurses. Some have shown more promising results than others.

The prenatal/early infancy project in New York, for instance, was set up in the late 1970s to provide an enhanced programme of home visits (nine in the antenatal period and continuing contact by the same midwife for up to two years after the birth) to pregnant teenagers, lone mothers and those who were unemployed or welfare recipients. The visits included health education, together with emotional and practical support in preparing for labour and childcare, as well as help in tackling financial and social problems as they arose.

Comparison between groups receiving the enhanced programme of visits and controls receiving normal screening and care at clinics showed that, among unmarried women living in poverty, those receiving systematic social support returned to school more rapidly after delivery, obtained more help with childcare and had fewer pregnancies over the next four years. There were also fewer cases of child abuse among the women at greatest risk. Heavier babies and fewer preterm births were recorded among nurse-visited women who were under 17 and those who were smokers. There was also a general finding of better knowledge and use of community services by visited women, and fewer accidents among their children (Olds *et al.*, 1986; 1988).

Other studies have failed to show significant effects on physical health, but have found beneficial psychological and behavioural effects. For example, a review of fourteen controlled trials of social support in pregnancy concluded that there was consistent evidence that women receiving support were less likely than controls to feel unhappy, nervous and worried during pregnancy, and less likely to have negative feelings about the forthcoming birth. After birth, supported women were less likely to be unhappy and more likely to be breastfeeding (Elbourne *et al.*, 1989).

In Edinburgh experiments in altering the course of postnatal depression by health visitors offering a series of counselling and social support visits have had some success in hastening recovery in women in disadvantaged conditions (Holden *et al.*, 1989). The accumulated evidence indicates that it is possible, using social support and carefully designed services, to help people to cope with stress – whether personal or environmental in origin (Oakley, 1992). The challenge is to extend such services to everyone who needs them.

In the UK several experiments in home-based strategies to help parents be more self-confident and skilful in their child's development have been initiated. One of the largest initiatives has been the child development programme, directed from the University of Bristol. This uses specially trained health visitors in areas of deprivation to build up parents' self-confidence, foster their skills in language stimulation for their children, and encourage early educational development, better nutrition and preventive health care. The stated aim is to encourage parental initiative, rather than lecture them on what they should and should not do (Barker and Anderson, 1988). Although initial evaluation by the project team has shown improvements in health and home environments for the children, no assessment has yet been made of the effects on the parents in the study. There is concern that although the essence of the approach is couched in terms of empowerment, it may be patronising or victim blaming in practice if not carefully administered.

To overcome some of these objections, an adaptation of the programme has been employed in Dublin, in which community mothers instead of professionals have been trained to give support and encouragement to parents. Among other effects, an evaluation found that mothers in the intervention group reported greater feelings of self-esteem than those in the control group. They also had more positive feelings about their child's first year (Johnson *et al.*, 1993; Lloyd, 1993).

Summary

A high proportion of studies that have set out to test the effectiveness of various interventions to tackle inequalities in health fall into policy level 1: aimed at strengthening individuals. Furthermore, many initiatives in this category are focused on behavioural factors rather than strengthening individuals against other determinants of health in the physical or social environment. Nevertheless, there are effective interventions at this level, albeit within the limited field chosen for the studies.

Interventions with a behavioural focus stand more chance of success if information giving is supplemented with personal support or structural changes that help make the behavioural change easier, and if the advice given is sensitive to the difficult circumstances in which many people live. A major problem with such interventions so far is that many attempts have been insensitive and tend to 'blame the victim', risking being counterproductive in the long run. The same could be said for interventions with an individual empowerment focus. Some espouse 'empowerment' in name, but fail to respect the self-esteem and dignity of participants. However, the better-quality ones have shown that, in the short term, some programmes can result in a more positive experience for women during pregnancy, childbirth and early motherhood, including reduced use of pain relief in labour and more active involvement in decisions about their health care. In the longer term there are indications that positive effects may extend to the health and wellbeing of the children in terms of, for example, better nutrition, fewer accidents, less childhood morbidity, higher rates of uptake of preventive care and so on. As yet the evidence is more suggestive than conclusive, and the relatively small-scale nature of the initiatives taken so far means that they are unlikely to have a major effect on overall inequalities in health. In any case, there is only so much that initiatives aimed at strengthening individuals can achieve in this respect, faced as they are with the weight of adverse factors outside individual control.

Strengthening communities

The second policy level can cover a wide spectrum of strategies aimed at strengthening the way disrupted and deprived communities function collectively for mutual support and benefit. These range from helping to create relaxing meeting places and facilities for social interaction to assisting mutual support to develop from within a community, using community development techniques. In its purest form, community development is essentially about increasing the ability of marginalised communities to work together to identify and take action on priorities defined as important by the communities themselves.

How might these initiatives influence inequalities in health? In theory, if people in marginalised communities were working well collectively they could influence their local environment in small but constructive ways: attracting resources to the area to improve housing and safety, for example, or working together to tackle crime or to limit substance abuse, or any other of their chosen priorities. These could lead to improvements in both physical and mental health in specific areas in the long run. In practice, the process of strengthening communities has proved highly complex, as the following examples show.

Community development programmes

Community development projects triggered by concern for poor health in deprived areas started to be funded in the 1970s in Britain. There are now about forty well-established ones, funded by charities, health and local authorities, as well as numerous smaller initiatives incorporating community development techniques to varying degrees. Some floundered and came to grief fairly early on in their development, but others have shown impressive achievements in terms of strengthening social networks, fostering skills of residents in dealing with health issues, and opening up channels of communication between professionals and residents resulting in more responsive and accessible local services (Youd and Jayne, 1986; Community Projects Foundation, 1988; Drummond, 1989; Ginnety *et al.*, 1989; Hunt, 1989). Some studies have also registered favourable changes in behavioural factors in communities resulting from project activities, although this was not their primary objective. Box 3.2 uses the Granton community health project in Scotland as a case study to illustrate how the many strands of the project have slowly evolved.

Similar processes and achievements have been documented for many other community development projects around the UK. In the Croxteth health action area in Liverpool, for example, residents set up credit unions and ran a successful campaign for a community centre, a drop-in centre and training in counselling and other skills (Thornley, 1992). Residents identified the dirty and dangerous state of the local environment as a major issue of concern. Environmental clean-up campaigns and land reclamation for children's play space resulted from their efforts. Initiatives stimulated within the earlier Waterloo health project in London included the fostering of community support networks. This included the development of a mental health drop-in centre, a mothers and toddlers drop-in centre, and a counselling group. In addition, residents organised several campaigns to combat the decline of the area – to prevent the closure of local schools, to develop the area with family housing rather than offices, and to convert a disused building into a sports and community centre (Waterloo Health Project, 1983). Several community development initiatives involving Asian communities around Rochdale, Cleveland and Manchester have demonstrated positive outcomes in terms of increased resident participation and decision making in urban renewal. The physical environment of some of the areas has been transformed – with traffic calming schemes, face-lifts and the creation of play areas. Residents have also played a vital role in the development of community amenities in their neighbourhoods. For example, the Sparth community centre was built to a design worked out by the community's own architect, balancing the needs of white and Asian residents, for instance, in terms of provision for religious activities and social events (Ellis, 1989).

There are, however, common problems encountered by community development interventions as well as achievements (Ellis, 1989; Hunt, 1993; McCormack, 1993). These include:

- resentment expressed by some residents that their neighbourhood was being stigmatised by being designated as a deprived area;

- disillusionment of local residents when they see projects come and go, having stayed long enough to raise hopes but not long enough for concrete improvements to materialise;

- conflict between the funding body, with one set of priorities, and the community if different priority needs are identified by residents;

- backlashes from other deprived communities when they believe that the project area has been given preferential treatment and has attracted scarce resources, to the detriment of other equally deprived areas;

Box 3.2: Strengthening communities in Scotland

A community development project was set up in the early 1980s in Granton, a deprived neighbourhood of Edinburgh, funded by the Scottish Home and Health Department and the Scottish Health Education Group (RUHBC, 1989; Hunt, 1993). It was staffed by a community development worker, a health visitor and, later, a research worker. Several community groups were formed with the project workers' encouragement on topics of concern to local residents; some were short-lived but others had far-reaching effects. For example, the women's health group started by looking at topics such as stress, childbirth and communication with doctors, but moved on to focus on the damp and mouldy housing conditions on the estate, which they feared might be affecting their health. They eventually prepared a tape-slide presentation, showing the problem and how it was affecting their lives, which was presented to a seminar at Edinburgh University at which they challenged researchers to respond to the problem. As a result, controlled research studies of damp housing and health status were carried out, first in Edinburgh and then confirmed in a large-scale, three-city study. These found strong and statistically significant links between the presence of damp and emotional distress in women and reports of respiratory and gastrointestinal problems and infections in children (Martin et al., 1987; Platt et al., 1989).

Tenants' groups from all over Edinburgh used the findings in their city-wide campaign for better housing. The results were also used by other groups from disadvantaged areas in Glasgow and Liverpool to persuade housing authorities to renovate some of their damp properties and to monitor improvements in residents' health. In Glasgow tenants used the research to enlist the support of the European Community for a solar energy demonstration project, to test ways of creating warm, dry dwellings with low heating costs. This was a rare example of lay people stimulating academic research on an issue identified as important by the community – and developing their political power in response.

The Granton residents went on to take other health-related initiatives. A major concern of local women was found to be their dependence on tranquillisers and anti-depressants. A tranquilliser withdrawal group was therefore set up, with members giving mutual support. All the regular members of the group eventually gave up the drugs, but continued to help new recruits and to look for ways to prevent mental health problems developing in the community. Following the offer of a house, rent free, for two days a week, the group set up a stress centre, operating on an informal drop-in basis. Two of the original members of the group found paid employment in staffing the centre (Hunt, 1989).

Groups evolving out of the needs of older people in the community ranged from a swimming club to a fruit and vegetable co-operative, and then on to the setting up of an 'elderly forum' to bring together pensioners and local professionals. This forum collected and presented the views of older residents to policy makers on ways of improving local services, but went a step further in using the information collected to secure urban aid funding to address some of the problems they had identified. The funding was able to cover the provision of a minibus and driver to ease transport problems, the appointment of an information worker on pensioners' issues, and a co-ordinator to organise a voluntary visiting scheme for frail elderly people returning home from hospital. The steering group for these developments was drawn from older people in the community (RUHBC, 1989).

- distress and feelings of impotence when residents realise the size of the problem and that the solution may not lie in the hands of that community.

All these problems demonstrate the sensitive and complex nature of community development, and how easily it can be mismanaged if there are misunderstandings about what is realistic for such a project to achieve with a given amount of time and resources. Those that have had realistic goals and sufficient time and support have shown that they can generate solid benefits for disadvantaged communities.

Community regeneration

Going beyond community development, which has traditionally been concerned with strengthening the way the social dynamics work in a community, there have been a number of experiments falling under the heading of 'community regeneration strategies'. These focus on multiply deprived areas with typically about 10–20,000 residents. They attempt to improve the social conditions in a neighbourhood at the same time as stimulating the local economy to provide more employment opportunities and tackling defects in the physical environment. The aim is to achieve sustainable and long-term improvements, acknowledging that three aspects – physical environment, economic opportunities and social conditions in a neighbourhood – are all inter-related and therefore a co-ordinated approach is essential.

In a review of community regeneration strategies in eight cities in the UK and Germany, carried out for the Joseph Rowntree Foundation, elements of such programmes to be avoided were identified, as well as ones that appear to offer prospects for success (see Box 3.3). The Foundation is now calling for the creation of a national community regeneration network of 200 designated zones to present a concerted and co-ordinated effort to tackle the problems of the neighbourhoods requiring the most urgent attention (Thake and Staubach, 1993).

In all this it should be recognised that, while revitalising communities by community development and regeneration is important, complementary action operating at policy level 3 could increase effectiveness in the long run. For example, empowering communities by strengthening the rights of all citizens, including entitlement to services and accessible complaints procedures, could play a useful part.

Improving access to essential facilities and services

In industrialised countries as well as in developing ones, improvements in day-to-day living and working conditions and access to services have been shown to be beneficial for the health of populations. Initiatives at this third level include some of the classic public health measures to improve access to adequate housing, sanitation, uncontaminated food supplies, safer workplaces and health and welfare services. A crucial point as regards inequalities in health is that such measures have the potential to benefit the health of the population in general, but especially that of the people living in the worst conditions, bringing about a reduction in the health gap.

Some of the most important level 3 policy initiatives are such well-established features of contemporary life in Britain that it is easy to take them for granted and leave them out of the

Box 3.3: Community regeneration strategies

A study of community regeneration programmes in eight cities in Germany and the UK concluded that interventions stood a better chance of success if they incorporated certain key elements, including:

- promoting strong citizen groups;

- co-ordinating and integrating programmes;

- giving priority to creating employment opportunities and combating poverty;

- establishing a sense of partnership between the participants;

- giving long-term commitment;

- allocating adequate and protected resources.

Conversely, there were elements to be avoided as they did not give rise to sustainable community regeneration. These include programmes that:

- consist predominantly of physical refurbishment;

- put physical programmes before local capacity building;

- have a short timescale;

- do not leave behind a locally managed infrastructure.

Source: Adapted from Thake and Staubach (1993)

equation when considering future options. To avoid this, it is useful to be reminded of the historical significance of such measures in the observed improvement in health, and the need to safeguard these achievements in the future. Assessment in this area is largely based on informed analyses of trends, but the importance of some of these achievements can also usefully be demonstrated by current experiments in third-world countries, as outlined below.

There is also a big new agenda at this level, concerned not only with securing the prerequisites for health in the physical environment but also with tackling the psychosocial health hazards encountered in day-to-day life. A brief mention is made here of the new agenda in housing, education and health care, before going on to a more detailed case study on healthier workplaces. This section then ends with an assessment of the significance of initiatives at this level for tackling inequalities in health in the future.

Safeguarding historical achievements

Richard Doll's (1992) analysis summarises the factors and policies that have, in his judgement, been influential in bringing about the striking improvements in health in industrialised countries over the century. He cites the reduction in the risk of, or fatality from, infection as the main factor in the decline in mortality, brought about by the rise in living standards, certain agricultural developments and extensive public health measures, including:

- improvements in nutrition, not only through greater purchasing power but also through the widespread introduction of better systems for the distribution and preservation of food, e.g., pasteurisation of milk;

- smaller family size due to fertility control;

- better provision of water uncontaminated with faeces;

- increased education and the application of scientific knowledge, e.g., in the control of the vectors of diseases such as malaria, and in immunisation.

To that list has to be added measures to undo the negative effects of industrialisation, such as improvements in dangerous and debilitating working conditions and the appalling housing conditions caused by rapid urbanisation, which was a consequence of the industrial revolution in countries such as Britain (Wohl, 1983).

Globally, such public health measures are as important today as ever. The World Bank suggests that:

> governments must do more to promote a healthier environment, especially for the poor, who face greatly increased health risks from poor sanitation, insufficient and unsafe water supplies, poor personal and food hygiene, inadequate garbage disposal, indoor air pollution, and crowded and inferior housing. Collectively, these risks are associated with nearly 30 per cent of the global burden of disease.

(1993a, p. 9)

Based on what has been achieved in poor communities in developing countries in tackling these factors, it is estimated that much of this burden of disease could be prevented. On the subject of water supply and sanitation, for example, a review of 144 studies concluded that the impact on health of such provision is significant. From the more rigorous studies it was calculated that a median reduction in child mortality of 55 per cent was associated with improved water supply and sanitation. In addition, the reductions achieved in disease severity were substantial and were sometimes greater than reductions in incidence (Esrey *et al.*, 1990; Huttly, 1990).

Such studies also serve to emphasise the health gains achieved by earlier public health interventions in industrialised countries. Even though greatly improved physical living and working conditions have been achieved, there is still a need to be continually vigilant in maintaining these gains, as demonstrated by the recent resurgence of tuberculosis in urban areas in Britain and of cholera and other infectious diseases in central and eastern Europe as public health standards slip (Spence *et al.*, 1993; WHO, 1994).

The new agenda

In western countries there are still evident problems of differentials in access to decent living conditions between different social groups, not just in terms of physical conditions but increasingly in the psychosocial environment. For example, the experience of living on a peripheral housing estate can be profoundly depressing, even with clean water and sanitation (McCormack, 1993). Fear of crime in unsafe streets and lack of recreation facilities can severely damage mental and social health, as well as limiting opportunities for physical activity, and the housing agenda for the future needs to address access to decent housing redefined in terms of modern-day problems. This is discussed further in Chapter 4.

As far as access to education is concerned, the focus in industrialised countries has changed from boosting overall literacy levels to answering more specific questions, such as, can the educational disadvantages associated with growing up in poverty be prevented or ameliorated? If they could, might there be knock-on effects in terms of health, wealth and social development? On this issue, there have been a variety of initiatives with this aim since the mid-1960s and long-term follow-up of children participating in the early experiments has taken place in the USA and Canada. The best-known programme of this kind is Head Start which began in 1965, targeting resources at the start on half a million children in the poorest counties in the USA. Twenty years later it was still helping 450,000 children. It was designed to be a comprehensive package of services providing early education at a day centre, immunisations, medical checkups to detect hearing and vision defects, hot meals during the day, and social services and parental education/support for the families of the children.

In practice there has been great variation in the scope and quality of the schemes set up, with some much better than others. Controlled studies have found consistently positive results for the better-quality, more comprehensive schemes. For example, the health of children participating in such schemes improved compared to controls in terms of increased immunisation rates, better diet and dental health, increased access to services, and improved self-esteem and cognitive abilities (McKey et al., 1985).

In terms of educational achievement, a follow-up of children who had participated in eleven preschool programmes found that they were significantly less likely than controls to have failed a grade in school or to have been put into special education classes (Lazar et al., 1982). The longer-term results of one particularly impressive programme showed higher rates of employment and entry into college, and lower rates of arrest and teenage pregnancies among the programme participants than in controls (Schweinhart et al., 1993).

The American evidence on comprehensive early education and services therefore holds out the prospect of significant benefits, both for the children concerned and for society in general. As the 1985 report of the US Committee for Economic Development concluded:

> *it would be hard to imagine that society could find a higher yield for a dollar of investment than that found in preschool programs for its at-risk children.*

(Schorr, 1988, p. 196)

The achievements made by many European countries in improving access to health and social welfare services have also been important at policy level 3. With rates of ill health increasing with decreasing socioeconomic status, the reduction of financial, cultural and geographic barriers to access to care could have substantial benefits in terms of relief of pain and suffering, as well as recovery and promotion of health, for more socially disadvantaged groups as outlined in Chapter 7.

Cost containment in health care has been at the top of the agenda for much of the 1980s in Europe and North America. As far as closing the gap in health between different social groups is concerned, American evidence on expanding and then cutting subsidised birth control services to women with low incomes is of particular interest because a reduction in the number of early or unplanned pregnancies has the potential to influence many aspects of health, including maternal nutrition, mortality and morbidity, as well as infant and childhood health. There is also the potential for an effect on the standard of living, with associated health benefits. From the late 1960s to the early 1980s access to subsidised birth control services in the USA was expanded. In parallel with this increase there was a significant narrowing of the gap in contraceptive use between black and white women and between women with more and less formal education, attributed in part to the federally supported programmes (Schorr, 1988). Since the early 1980s, however, there has been a substantial decrease in funding for these services. A study of the years 1976–90 revealed that spending dropped by 21 per cent, leading to a reduction in the numbers of patients served and an increase in the variation between states in the provision of services to women with low incomes – increasing geographic inequalities in provision unrelated to measures of need. There were also indications that the quality of services may also have declined, with fewer sessions per site and cutbacks on evening and weekend sessions. Many agencies had cut their outreach programmes, which recruited and followed up high-risk and hard-to-reach groups, and McFarlane and Meier (1993) concluded that cuts in federal public health funding fell disproportionately on people living in poverty and threatened their health. This is but one example of the benefits of access to essential services at this policy level, and the importance of looking at where the effects of cuts in services fall most heavily.

Case study: healthier workplaces

As a number of aspects of level 3 policies are covered in Chapter 4 (housing), Chapter 5 (social security provision), and Chapter 7 (access to health care), the new agenda for working conditions has been singled out for closer inspection here.

Important improvements in physical working conditions have been made throughout the century, for example concerning safety, excessive hours of work, employment of children and exposure to damaging substances. These are examples of successful policies to reduce social inequalities in health, as exposure to such health hazards in the workplace was greatest in the most disadvantaged social and economic groups. However, there is still a social gradient in working conditions in industrialised countries, with the focus now on psychosocial as well as physical hazards. The lower the occupational class, for example, the more likely are people to experience physical strain, serious injury, higher noise and air pollution levels, unsocial hours, a monotonous job and a forced pace of work with few voluntary pauses (Hasan, 1989). There has been growing concern that certain production processes introduced in the postwar period in Europe and America have caused a deterioration in working conditions by introducing alienating and dehumanising conditions in an attempt to increase productivity. The combination of stress and lack of social support that they engender can have damaging effects on psychosocial health and safety, as well as being risk factors for cardiovascular disease.

The work factors resulting in the highest cardiovascular risk are those where people have little control over how they meet the job's demands and how they use their skills, coupled with little emotional support or feedback from superiors and fellow workers. These conditions are found to be more common among workers with low-status jobs, many of whom are rated as having psychological demands as heavy as those of executives, but who lack the freedom to make decisions about how to do their work. As Karasek's and Theorell's (1990) work shows, it is not the bosses but the people who are bossed about who suffer most from work stress.

It has been postulated that part of the association between social position and the risk of cardiovascular illness may be due to differences in psychosocial work conditions, which may affect the risk through either neuroendocrine mechanisms or lifestyle. For example, excessive tobacco consumption may be a way of coping with poor working conditions (Marmot and Theorell, 1988). This analysis is useful because it suggests practical possibilities for doing something about the inequalities caused by such working conditions. Karasek (1992) has suggested that theoretically there are four main points of intervention in the prevention of stress related to working conditions, and these roughly correspond to the four policy levels discussed in this chapter. First, there are person-based approaches, offering counselling and education to increase an individual's skill and capacity to cope with the stress produced by the work set-up. Obviously, this treats the symptoms rather than the cause of the problem. Secondly, there are improvements in communication patterns and human relations, providing more opportunities for making decisions, joint problem solving with colleagues and constructive feedback on how the job is going. Thirdly, there are large-scale organisational changes, such as redesigning production processes and management strategies that influence the tasks individual workers are asked to do. Fourthly, there are changes to outside pressures, such as market conditions, rules about competition and national labour relations programmes, which are largely outside a company's control.

In practice, different countries have used different approaches. American experiments in this field, for example, have been predominantly concerned with the person-based coping skills end of the spectrum, whereas the Scandinavian countries have tended to redesign the environment in which people work (Karasek and Theorell, 1990).

The International Labour Office (1992) has recently collected together and analysed nineteen international case studies on stress prevention through work reorganisation, covering all four approaches, illustrated in Box 3.4. The general conclusion is that it is possible to make improvements in working conditions in such a way as to reduce the risk of work stress. It is also important to note that the methods appear to work best in the manual and low-status occupations with the highest risk of psychosocial stress, providing further encouragement that this might be a fruitful line of action. However, to date, most of the initiatives have been confined to separate workplaces and the scale of the operations has not been sufficient to measure or influence changes in health indicators across occupational groups. There needs to be political commitment at the highest levels to encourage larger-scale changes. Much progress on this front has been made by Sweden, as detailed on page 48.

Summary

This section has argued that interventions at policy level 3 – improving access to essential facilities and services – have had great historical significance in reducing inequalities in health in Britain, and their continuing importance can be demonstrated by evidence from

Box 3.4: Improving psychosocial conditions in the workplace

The International Labour Office (ILO) (1992) has reviewed nineteen international case studies of attempts to improve stress related to the workplace. These included such experiments as increasing variety and understanding of the different tasks in a production process, workforce participation in the identification of problems and their solutions, and changing shift patterns to make them less tiring and disruptive to workers' personal lives. The evidence shows that it is possible to make improvements in psychosocial factors by tailoring changes to specific workplaces. For example, in the nine case studies in which stress symptoms were monitored, eight reported improvement in response to stress. Ten cases noted a reduction in the specific work problems identified at the initiation of the programmes. Thirteen cases showed significant improvement in organisational changes considered likely to lead to stress reduction (Karasek, 1992).

Some fairly commonsense factors were noted as associated with success in these programmes: the level of effort put into the programme and management's willingness to take risks; joint management/labour support; active involvement of workers in planning or significant worker participation in group discussions on environmental changes and type of occupation, with the greatest success occurring in skilled craft or operators' jobs and lower-level service and clerical workers. Less success was reported in experiments involving managers and professional workers, where conditions were already relatively good.

Another spin-off from some stress prevention programmes has been gains in productivity, particularly when the programme involved significant changes in work organisation. Six of the twelve ILO cases where productivity was recorded showed gains in productivity and two further cases showed significant future possibilities for gains. Similarly, the Volvo plant in Göteburg has recorded increases in productivity following psychosocial job redesign, as well as reductions in psychosomatic and gastrointestinal problems (Karasek and Theorell, 1990).

developing countries today. However, it should not be assumed that industrialised countries have solved the main problems of providing the prerequisites for health universally. A number of subsequent chapters illustrate that much remains to be done in contemporary Britain, for example, to improve access to decent housing and appropriate health care as well as tackling poverty. In addition, new kinds of problems are emerging concerning psychosocial as much as physical living and working conditions. These demand renewed effort with a new agenda. The detailed case study of creating healthier workplaces was used to illustrate the types of interventions that have been attempted in this area and the most promising approaches emerging from the evaluations. However, as yet they have been applied on a relatively small and piecemeal scale within specific industries.

Encouraging macroeconomic and cultural change

Policy level 4 includes the macroeconomic and social policies that span many sectors. The former are concerned, for example, with how a government chooses to stimulate economic growth, how it deals with balance-of-payments and budgetary deficits, and the control of inflation. Policy measures employed typically include tough controls on the money supply and government spending. Social policies at this level also have a great bearing on such factors as the standard of living of the poorest sections of the population, the level of unemployment and the promotion of equal opportunities.

Following the approach of comparing different countries and different periods of time, it has been shown that countries that have implemented economic policies that have (by design or accident) reduced poverty and brought about a more equal distribution of resources have made most progress in certain key aspects of health, such as life expectancy and infant mortality, as discussed below.

Developing countries

In relation to developing countries, for example, the World Bank's *World Development Report 1993* analysed the dramatic decline in mortality, particularly steep since 1950. It concluded that 'advances in income and education have allowed households almost everywhere to improve their health' (p. 7). Macroeconomic policy that increased income was seen to work by increasing the ability of people to obtain 'the prerequisites for health': food, housing, warmth, safe water, satisfying employment and so on. According to this analysis, certain government and state policies represented at levels 3 and 4 stand out as bringing about marked improvements in health in developing countries:

- economic growth policies that benefited people living in poverty and preserved cost-effective health expenditure;
- investments in specified public health measures and essential clinical services;
- investments in schooling, particularly for girls;
- policies that helped promote the rights and status of women, increasing their political and economic power and giving them protection against abuse (World Bank, 1993a).

The Bank came to these conclusions on good investments for health after reviewing evidence from a variety of sources. First, in global terms, the strong positive correlation between a country's average per capita income and life expectancy was acknowledged, particularly marked in developing countries, but tapering off in richer countries. Analysis of this relationship in twenty-two developing countries suggested that the main effect of economic growth on life expectancy was through successful poverty reduction policies and increased spending on public health measures.

Secondly, the importance of policies to influence the distribution of resources within a country is recognised, based on examination of policy in countries and regions that have achieved better health status than expected from their economic position. Rich countries like Japan and poorer countries such as China, Costa Rica and Sri Lanka have all made impressive improvements in life expectancy and infant mortality, which appear to be associated with the more equal distribution of income that accompanied economic growth in these countries.

Conversely, the unhealthiness of various economic policies pursued within countries, and advocated for other countries in times of economic crisis, has become more obvious, not least from studies of the effects of western banking initiatives to tackle third-world debt.

Economic adjustment policies linked to western aid, for instance, have often recommended boosting the export sector while cutting government spending, with the axe likely to fall on health-related expenditure as a result. As the World Bank now emphasises, in many countries 'early cuts were indiscriminate and failed to preserve those elements of the health system with the strongest long-term benefits for health' (1993a, p. 45). Furthermore, the impact of such cuts tended to fall most heavily on the most disadvantaged sections of the population. In some cases the poor have got poorer, malnutrition has increased, fewer children are in school, and health care and clean water are less available than before (Abel-Smith, 1986; Logie and Woodroffe, 1993; UNICEF, 1993).

Industrialised countries

In industrialised countries, having economic policies that reduce poverty may be just as important for public health. Cross-national comparisons of health trends in OECD countries have shown a strong correlation between more equitable income distribution and improvements in overall life expectancy (Wilkinson, 1992). This work raises the possibility that the overall health profile of a country may be influenced by inequitable income distribution, not just the health of the most disadvantaged sections of the population.

As yet, there is a lack of cross-national comparisons of what happens to social inequalities in health within countries as income distribution varies, but the relationship between health indicators and specific economic and social policies has been analysed at the international level. For example, a comparison of eighteen industrialised countries over the period 1950–85 looked at changes in infant mortality, income distribution and public policy aiming to compensate families and people who are unemployed for loss of income. This study found that the level of economic development had a strong but decreasing impact on the infant mortality rate. For rich countries, the degree of inequality in income distribution, especially the standard of living among the less well off, seemed to be very important for 'explaining' statistically the rate of infant mortality. High rates of universal family benefits were linked to relatively low rates of infant mortality. Conversely, when countries had a large proportion of people unemployed with inadequate social security benefits this was associated with a higher infant mortality rate (Wennemo, 1993). Wennemo's conclusion was that an effective policy for lowering infant mortality rates may be to make the distribution of economic resources more equal and to preserve an adequate level of social security for vulnerable groups. Studies in Sweden also point to public policies that prevent substantial income loss, for example during unemployment, as important tools in public health policy (Lundberg and Fritzell, 1994).

The reverse of such an economic and social strategy has been pursued in Britain and several other industrialised countries during the 1980s. The goals of reducing balance-of-payments deficits and inflation while promoting the political aims of privatisation and shifts towards more market-oriented systems, have been pursued by measures such as cuts in government social spending and casualisation of low-paid work, together with changes to the tax system favouring the richer sections of society. Rising unemployment has added to the critical situation. The result has been rising numbers in poverty, coupled with deteriorating absolute income among the poor. Simultaneously, rises in the relative incomes of those who were already rich increased income inequalities dramatically. An analysis of the impact of the 1988 social security reforms in Britain showed that overall spending on means-tested benefits had fallen by 6 per cent. Almost half the poorest 20 per cent of households had become worse off due to these reforms. The losers included most people who were unemployed and the poorest childless households, as well as half of all lone-parent families and more than one in three couples with children. Although older people, people with a long-term illness and families with children did benefit from higher targeted benefits, much of the gain was taken away by new requirements on them to pay a proportion of their rent or poll tax (Evans *et al.*, 1994). The overall result of these and similar changes over the period 1979–91, has been a fall of 14 per cent in real disposable income for the poorest 10 per cent of the population, while tax and other changes have produced a more than 60 per cent increase in income for the richest 10 per cent of the population (HC Debates, 1993).

National evidence about whether the observed widening income differentials over the 1980s have been accompanied by a widening gap in mortality between different social groups will not be available for a few more years, but more local studies give some indication of a worsening situation in some areas. For example, a study of electoral wards in the Northern Regional Health Authority area of England in the years between 1981 and 1991 showed a substantial increase in the differentials in infant and adult mortality and in low birthweight between the most and least deprived wards, coupled with widening social and economic differences between the wards (Phillimore and Beattie, 1994; Phillimore *et al.*, 1994). A similar worsening of the mortality gap between affluent and deprived neighbourhoods in Glasgow has been observed over the 1980s (Forwell, 1992; McCarron *et al.*, 1994). Furthermore, there is evidence that the postcode sectors throughout Scotland that were categorised as deprived in 1981 were relatively more deprived by the 1991 census. The mortality experience of the deprived localities, relative to either Scotland or affluent neighbourhoods, worsened over the same period (McLoone and Boddy, 1994).

In the USA similar economic and welfare policies introduced in the 1970s and accelerated in the 1980s have resulted in widening differentials in income between the black and white populations (Hacker, 1992), which has been followed by a widening gap in life expectancy (Rogers, 1992). As yet evidence such as this is only suggestive, but points to areas for urgent study.

At this policy level it is important to note that there are growing challenges to the notion that increasing income inequality is necessary for economic growth. In a recent analysis of the reasons behind the 'economic miracle' achieved in eight east Asian countries (including Japan, South Korea and Thailand), the World Bank (1993b) concluded that rapid economic growth in these countries had not been achieved by widening the gap between rich and poor. In fact, over the period of growth income inequality declined by as much as or more than in other comparable developing countries.

Others have gone further and investigated whether more equal income distribution is a precondition for growth. Rodrik (1994), for example, has reanalysed the World Bank data and found that the 'miracle' countries all started with a more equal income distribution and very high school-enrolment rates compared with other developing countries. These two factors explained statistically about 90 per cent of the higher economic growth subsequently achieved by the east Asian countries, and suggest that more equal societies that invest significantly in education for the population tend to grow faster. This finding needs to be corroborated, but at the very least the evidence confirms that more equitable income distribution in a country does not harm the economy, and may even benefit it. It certainly benefits people living in poverty in more ways than one.

Summary

Evidence at policy level 4 from both the developing and the industrialised world suggests that there can be 'healthy' and 'unhealthy' economic policies (Dahlgren, 1993). The impact of macroeconomic policies on the health of the most vulnerable groups in society therefore needs to be monitored carefully.

Poverty reduction policies are potentially very important for tackling inequalities in health and, as discussed in greater detail in Chapter 5, these would entail both ameliorating the effects of hardship through adequate social security provision for those who fall into poverty, and attempts to prevent poverty in the long term.

More strategic approaches

The above discussion gives examples of attempts to tackle inequalities in health at different policy levels and from a variety of entry points: focusing on certain age groups; specific diseases; and particular determinants of health such as living and working conditions. There are, however, some examples of attempts that have tried to take a more strategic approach, with some co-ordination of policies across sectors and between levels.

A strategic approach is potentially important for tackling inequalities in health because the differentials are caused by inter-related social and economic factors. Tackling one aspect without doing anything about linked factors may therefore not produce optimum results. The importance of having a co-ordinated intersectoral strategy can be well illustrated in relation to community regeneration programmes for multiply deprived neighbourhoods.

> *Improvements to the physical fabric, which do not address underlying economic problems, can be short-lived. Economic initiatives which do not recognise the depressed state of many people living in deprived communities and the lack of adequate skills among the residents will struggle to take off. Training and capacity building which is not linked into realistic opportunities of jobs or additional responsibility will not be seen to be relevant.*
> (Thake and Staubach, 1993, p. 22)

Evidence that strategic approaches are now being attempted at international, national and more local levels is detailed below, illustrating the wide scope for immediate action if the commitment is there.

International

At the international level, the European Region of WHO has led the way since 1985 with its Health for All strategy, which has as its central aim to ensure greater social equity in health (WHO, 1985). To achieve this aim it has advocated co-ordinated policies in each country directed at:

- reducing poverty in its widest sense;
- securing the basic prerequisites for health for everybody – food, safe water, sanitation, decent housing and universal education;
- ensuring that everybody has access to effective health care.

WHO has consistently lobbied to persuade national and local governments to adopt a Health for All approach, and can claim considerable success in raising awareness of the issue and in getting policy makers to include commitments to tackle inequalities in health in their health strategies. Many of the more enthusiastic responses have come from local and regional governments, rather than from the national level. WHO has no legal or fiscal powers though, which limits the impact it can have in bringing about major changes in the direction it is advocating.

The European Community (EC), on the other hand, has considerable legal and fiscal powers to influence member states but did not have an official public health focus until 1993. Nevertheless, there have been strategic approaches taken to tackling issues which have the potential to influence inequalities in health. For example:

- the EC poverty programme;
- the social fund to stimulate infrastructure improvements and economic regeneration in more disadvantaged regions;
- the environmental programmes laying down standards for water safety;
- the social chapter of the Maastricht Treaty, aiming, among other things, to improve working conditions for those with least protection across the Community.

These all make a contribution, particularly at policy levels 3 and 4, but they would benefit from a more informed health input. There are also EC programmes which, although they have the potential, have not been used to promote equity in health. These include policies influencing the price, quality and distribution of food and alcohol, or tobacco growing and advertising. With co-ordinated action they could have a major impact. There is an opportunity now, with article 129 of the Maastricht Treaty, to develop co-ordinated policies which would tackle inequalities in health. Under this article, the EC is now legally obliged to encourage the improvement of public health in its member states. Most significantly, it has to consider the health impact of other EC policies, for example in agriculture and the environment, and to incorporate appropriate health protection requirements where necessary. If the impact of policies on the health of the most disadvantaged in society were taken as a measure, then the focus would be firmly on tackling inequalities in health.

National

At the national level, The Netherlands and Sweden are examples of countries that have taken a strategic approach to inequalities in health, but with very different ways of going about it. The Netherlands, stimulated in part by the Black Report and the WHO Health for All strategy, has taken a systematic research and consensus-building approach. In 1987, the Ministry of Welfare, Public Health and Culture, together with the Scientific Council for Government Policy, brought together key policy makers from all the political parties, from the trade unions and employers' organisations and from the health professions, to look at the available evidence and to agree on steps to be taken. The outcome was a five-year research programme, commissioned by the Ministry to inform policy making, to be carried out by combined efforts from all the universities in the country. Studies were initiated to document the extent and nature of social inequalities in health in The Netherlands and to make comparisons with other countries. Causal mechanisms were investigated, as well as the review commissioned of evaluated interventions from the world literature already discussed, and some fairly small demonstration projects were set up to evaluate how inequalities might be tackled at the local level.

During the period of that research programme, the Scientific Council for Government Policy again hosted a consensus conference, which agreed that the extent and possible widening of inequalities in health in The Netherlands warranted an integrated and interdisciplinary approach by various government departments and a range of statutory and non-statutory organisations. Most significantly, agreement was reached on the need to use an integrated approach to carry out assessments on major policy decisions. Their impact on the health of the people in poor socioeconomic circumstances was to be measured (WRR, 1991). A further five-year programme was agreed for 1993–97, with a shift in focus towards policy development and related research. The Dutch approach has therefore been one of slow but careful analysis, trying to keep all the main parties on board for the action phase (Mackenbach, 1994).

In Sweden, legislation and social welfare initiatives have been used extensively to tackle inequalities in infant mortality and in ill health related to the working environment. Housing programmes and high levels of income support and welfare provision for women and children have been part of the response to large inequalities in infant mortality observed in the 1930s (Diderichsen, 1990). In recent decades there has been a dramatic decrease in infant mortality for the population as a whole, as well as a narrowing of the gap between the different social groups, so that now there is only a small gap, with very low levels of mortality for all social groups by international standards (Dahlgren and Diderichsen, 1986; Leon et al., 1992). Disentangling which component of Swedish social policy has been the major contributor to this decline is another matter, but Wennemo's work (1993), outlined on page 44, points to strong associations between low infant mortality, more equal income distribution and extensive welfare support for families with children.

The strategic approach in Sweden is highly developed in relation to ill health and the workplace, stemming in part from the long-term association between the government and the labour unions. The government has supported extensive research in this field and has employed legislation to improve psychosocial as well as physical conditions in workplaces based on the findings. In addition, through the Swedish Working Life Fund (the equivalent of £1.5 billion), raised by a levy on business, the government has since 1991 been offering financial grants as incentives to companies to make improvements in the worst conditions in line with the legislation (Levi, 1992). This provides a valuable trial of how industrial attitudes and culture might be influenced on a national level. The unions representing manual workers responded to research showing higher mortality risks among manual occupational classes by setting up a five-year health programme in 1987 to improve health-related working conditions and opportunities for health promotion in the workplace (Lundberg, 1991).

On a wider front, there has been a concerted effort to push for health impact assessments on all public policies in Sweden. At the same time, a national institute was set up to develop and support intersectoral public health policies at local, regional and national levels, particularly related to disadvantaged sections of the population.

Several countries, including Australia, Canada, Finland and Wales, have made a commitment to tackling inequalities in health as a matter of priority when drawing up national health strategies and targets. In some cases, specific targets have been set to improve the health of identified disadvantaged groups (Health Promotion Authority for Wales, 1990; Nutbeam *et al.*, 1993; Whitehead *et al.*, 1993). This kind of differential target setting has also been carried out at regional health authority level in England. Oxford, in its ten-year health promotion strategy, proposed that resources should be focused on the poorest areas in the more disadvantaged districts within its boundaries. It employed community development approaches in intensive efforts in those areas and set differential targets by gender and social class (Griffiths *et al.*, 1991).

Cities and regions

At the city or regional level, some local authorities have formulated social or anti-poverty strategies in which they review all the services under the direct control of the council for the possible contribution each can make to the goal of reducing or preventing poverty. Added to this is an assessment of what advocacy role the council can realistically play in influencing central government policies and the actions of other local agencies outside the council's control. Perhaps the earliest and one of the most comprehensive examples in this area has been the work of the Strathclyde Regional Council, which first devised its social strategy in the 1970s. Box 3.5 summarises eight main components of the strategy, which include: those aimed at strengthening individuals to manage money and debt more effectively (level 1); others concerned with community development and support for the voluntary sector in specified areas of disadvantage (level 2); take-up campaigns to increase access to council and government welfare rights for immediate relief of poverty (level 3); and, an advocacy role in lobbying central government to implement poverty-reducing economic policy (level 4) (Strathclyde Regional Council, 1993).

Likewise, the recent anti-poverty strategy of Nottingham City Council attempts to co-ordinate the efforts of several departments, including housing, social services, environmental health and planning. It combines better targeting of council services to disadvantaged neighbourhoods with community, economic and social development of these areas. This includes attempts to reduce the barriers to employment experienced in certain disadvantaged areas, for example by better training, childcare and transport provision (Gale, 1994).

Similar examples could be given for other major cities around the country, together with some of the more intensive WHO healthy cities projects, which have been running since the mid-1980s (Tsouros, 1991). One criticism levelled at some of the healthy cities projects, however, is that although the reduction of inequalities in health is often a stated aim, in practice they seem to be restricted to initiatives at level 1 and, to a lesser extent, level 2. Some appear to be little more than health education projects – with a gesture towards community development, but without as yet harnessing the full potential of civic organisations to influence living and working conditions and access to services at level 3

Box 3.5: Strathclyde's strategic approach to poverty

The council's anti-poverty strategy can be summarised in eight approaches.

1 Maximising the provision of direct financial assistance to people living in poverty from sources under the council's control, e.g., clothing and footwear grants and public transport concessionary fares.

2 Providing welfare rights services and publicity to help people gain the state benefits to which they are entitled.

3 Providing money advice services to help those who fall into debt, while at the same time combating illegal money lending.

4 Promoting the development of credit unions and other community initiatives; supporting the role of voluntary and community sectors in addressing poverty.

5 Giving priority to people living in poverty in the delivery of council services that benefit them.

6 Collecting and disseminating a range of information on the extent of poverty in the region, trends, affected groups and comparisons with other areas, to inform policy making.

7 Requiring all departments and committees of the council to consider the implications of their policies upon people living in poverty, and assess the impact on poverty of any proposals for making savings or new service developments during the annual budget process.

8 Making representation to central government about the need to reduce poverty through measures to increase the number of jobs, tackle low pay and make changes in the benefit, taxation and criminal justice systems.

Source: Adapted from Strathclyde Regional Council (1993)

(Kelly *et al.,* 1993; Adams, 1994). In Chapter 7, the way Liverpool healthy cities project successfully addressed such criticisms is described.

What can we learn?

What emerges from this review of policy interventions of relevance to any future strategy aimed at reducing social inequalities in health? Above all, there is the very positive finding that there are some strategies at all policy levels that actually work – they reduce health hazards and improve opportunities for health among people experiencing poverty and various forms of social disadvantage. Some work better than others, and the analysis of why is crucially important.

At level 1, strengthening individuals, there are now effective interventions to promote change in behavioural factors in groups where prevalence is high. These rely on supportive education giving practical relevant advice, sensitive to the difficult circumstances in which people live, and – most importantly – aided by policies at other levels to create enabling environments. The shift in behaviour achieved by these more sensitive methods may still be less than could be achieved with more advantaged social groups using the same methods, as illustrated with the smoking in pregnancy interventions quoted on page 29. This re-emphasises the restrictions that low income and poor environments place on behaviour change, and also the need for wider supporting strategies.

However, when attention is paid to easing the harshness of the environment, there are examples of greater effects being achieved for sub-groups living in the very poorest conditions. The impact of combined nutrition education and supplementation programmes quoted on page 30, for example, was found to be greatest among a subset of the poorest women and children within the disadvantaged intervention groups.

Another key finding is that some strategies have the potential for a long-term impact on opportunities for health. The studies of social support of pregnant teenagers, for example, show a higher rate of return to school after the birth in some cases, and fewer pregnancies in subsequent years, in groups receiving support. Likewise, early education of preschool children from disadvantaged backgrounds, incorporating services to tackle physical, social and intellectual disabilities, suggests far-reaching effects on school drop-out rates, arrest rates, entry into further education and teenage pregnancy rates. However, because of the difficulty of evaluating effects over these long time periods, all these findings are tentative and require further confirmation. Some efforts also require a health warning: although they purport to empower individuals or communities, they risk being patronising and victim blaming if not undertaken with skill and sensitivity.

Interventions at policy levels 1 and 2 – strengthening individuals and communities – have often been focused on exclusive groups that are deprived, and have not involved wider sections of the population. They have also tended to treat the symptoms rather than the underlying cause of the problem, which may be located in the socioeconomic environment. Coupled with the fact that, so far, many of these have been discrete experiments or projects involving relatively few individuals and neighbourhoods, their overall impact on observed inequalities in health can only have been minimal. The challenge is to make the effective approaches more widespread, part of the mainstream services offered to people, not just limited to a few scattered projects.

In contrast, interventions at policy levels 3 and 4 involve every section of the population, although there can be a differential effect. Some of the improvements to living conditions and access to services, for example, can be seen to have benefited everyone, but most especially those subject to the worst conditions. The major public health works started in the last century to provide clean water and sanitation, the measures taken to provide universal education and health care, and to develop a comprehensive welfare system, have played an important part in improving overall health status. But they have also been of greatest benefit to those who previously faced financial barriers to access and those in the most insanitary, hazardous conditions.

Experience with policies at level 4, to bring about macroeconomic and cultural changes, shows the importance of looking at the distributional effects of policies as well as their aggregate impact. It is essential to monitor where the human costs and benefits of policies fall across the population. The experience with some of the early structural adjustment policies to deal with third-world debt, for example, show that the most vulnerable sections of the population sometimes carried the brunt of the costs in health terms. Conversely, economic policies that have protected or improved the standard of living of the poor have shown beneficial health effects, large enough sometimes to be reflected in health statistics for the population as a whole. The evidence suggests that some of the key policy requirements include:

- income maintenance policies that provide adequate financial support for people who fall into poverty;

- education and training policies that help prevent poverty in the long term;

- more equitable taxation and income distribution policies.

Finally, when considering policy options at the four different levels, the inter-relationships between levels stand out and need to be taken into account. There are clearly opportunities for initiatives to be taken at each level, but also a need for more strategic approaches incorporating action across sectors and at various policy levels. This is what has been missing in Britain so far.

CHAPTER 4

The housing dimension

Richard Best

Introduction

When nearly 1,000 residents on a poor council estate in Bristol were asked 'What do you think would improve your health or the health of those who live with you?', the most common replies were 'better housing' (30 per cent) or 'a better environment' (15 per cent) (Ineichen, 1993).

It may seem obvious that 'bad housing damages your health', but proving the case is not always easy. People who live in decaying, overcrowded properties are likely to be poor and face other disadvantages; the fact that they do not enjoy such good health as those in decent housing is clearly not attributable to housing conditions alone. People living in council housing are much more likely to die before the age of 65 than owner occupiers (Goldblatt, 1990b), but it may not be the council housing that has increased the mortality rates.

The aim of this chapter is to assess what changes should be made to public policy on housing to reduce inequalities in health. The chapter begins with a brief description of the types of housing problems experienced in Britain. It then reviews the latest evidence available on the link between poor housing and health. Finally, it describes and evaluates a range of policy options to improve housing in ways that will reduce inequalities in health.

Overview of housing problems

The nation's housing problems can be divided into two kinds: those of quantity and those of quality. Shortages of affordable accommodation lead to overcrowding and homelessness. In this section the extent of overcrowding and homelessness among two key groups, single people and families, is reviewed and the trends over the last decade are discussed. The problems of quality in British housing are considered next. Poor housing conditions are manifest in the numbers of properties declared unfit for habitation or lacking in essential amenities. The quality of the local environment is also of concern. The evidence in this area is summarised and consideration is given to the adequacy of the policy response.

Problems of quantity

Over the last twenty years overcrowding has diminished as a national issue. Landlords have been compelled to avoid overcrowding their premises, and the growth of owner occupation has been more likely to lead to problems of under-occupation. But 'houses in multiple occupation' remain at the bottom end of the private sector in which conditions are extremely poor (statistics are not entirely helpful because they include student and temporary housing, which may be suited to its purposes). Better enforcement of the overcrowding rules has led, in turn, to more people with nowhere to go: homelessness figures rose relentlessly from the mid-1970s to the early 1990s.

Homelessness: single people

Homelessness among single people is not the subject of clear recording. If this is taken to mean 'roofless', i.e. people sleeping rough, a count on census night reported relatively modest figures – 2,827 people in Great Britain (OPCS, 1991a) – although the Census Office acknowledges that this is an underestimate. Nevertheless, recent audits of street homelessness indicate that the numbers of people have fallen because of the government's rough sleepers initiative, which provided additional hostel and short-term rented property for people sleeping rough in central London. The London figure was down to around 500 – from its census count of 1,275 – by the autumn of 1993 (Brown and Randall, 1993). However, these figures mask the true extent of shortages: a far larger number of single people are homeless but remain hidden because they are sleeping on the floors of friends and relations, often moving from place to place. A study in the late 1980s estimated that in London alone there were at least 50,000 single people living in temporary accommodation (which might not necessarily be contrary to their wishes), or in squats or on the streets, with a further 74,000 living unwillingly as part of someone else's household (Eardley, 1989).

Surprisingly, the number of single people who are homeless in rural areas appears to be a special problem. A 1992 study for the Rural Development Commission that showed how homelessness among the statutorily defined groups had tripled in the previous four years, also indicated particular problems for young people for whom the figures are not recorded (Lambert et al., 1992).

The reasons why single people have left their previous accommodation are varied, but a study by the University of York indicated that 70 per cent of those living rough, and 50 per cent of those in hostels and bed-and-breakfast hotels, had previously been in some kind of institution such as a children's home, a prison or a psychiatric hospital (Anderson et al., 1993). Along with others who have left home because relationships have broken down, or are seeking work elsewhere, these single people have found that they cannot afford accommodation available on the open market.

Homelessness: families

Statistical evidence of housing shortages for families and other 'vulnerable' households is much better documented. Local authorities record the numbers of those whom they deem to have nowhere else to go, yet have not 'intentionally' made themselves homeless in order to gain priority for council housing. The number of such families showed a rapid increase

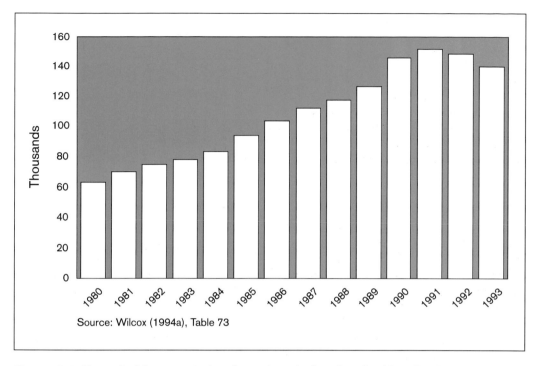

Figure 4.1: Households accepted as homeless by local authorities, England, 1980–93

from the time the statistics were first compiled in 1977 until 1991. As can be seen from Figure 4.1, the number of families declared homeless doubled between 1980 and 1990, but then fell slightly to 139,790 in 1993. These trends are, in part, a result of demographic factors. During the 1980s the 'baby boom' generation were entering their thirties, which resulted in the creation of more new households with consequent pressure on the housing supply, but by 1990, the 'baby bust' generation was emerging, which appears to have relieved this pressure (Ermisch, 1990).

More important than the total number of families declared homeless are those for whom the local authority has no available housing. Such households are moved into temporary accommodation, which has, notoriously, often meant bed-and-breakfast hotels. As Figure 4.2 shows, the number of households in bed-and-breakfast hotels and special hostels increased nearly fivefold between 1980 and 1991. Encouragingly, this figure has fallen quite sharply over the last two years, to just over 15,000 in 1993. This only partly reflects the drop in the numbers accepted as homeless by local authorities: it is more to do with greater use being made of accommodation in the private rented sector through various leasing arrangements. The number of families housed in this sector increased tenfold in the 1980s, from 4,200 in 1982 to over 44,000 in 1992, and then dropped slightly to 38,720 in 1993.

The numbers of people who are homeless give an indication of the severity of pressures for available accommodation. In themselves the numbers represent only a small proportion of the whole population, but these extreme cases represent the visible tip of an iceberg which includes far greater numbers of people. A series of studies has concluded that about 100,000 extra homes each year are needed to meet outstanding demands over and above

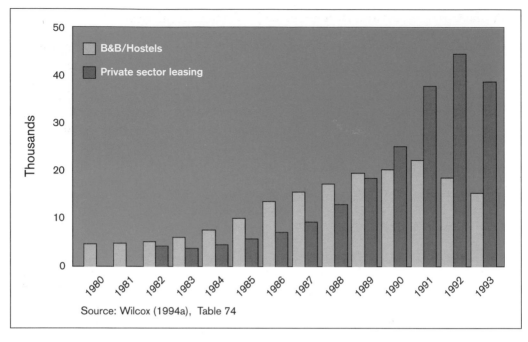

Source: Wilcox (1994a), Table 74

Figure 4.2: Households housed in temporary accommodation by local authorities, England, 1980–93

the predicted output of private developers and housing associations. The figure rises by at least 10,000 if the needs of single-person households are taken into account (Whitehead and Kleinman, 1992). The fact of the matter is that, even though demographic trends are now more favourable, continuing and accumulating shortages of housing can be predicted unless output is stepped up.

Problems of quality

The quality of housing has steadily improved throughout this century. The most recent survey of stock condition is the *English House Condition Survey 1991* (EHCS) (DoE, 1993). This showed that the number of dwellings lacking basic amenities had continued its downward fall, to 1 per cent of the stock (205,000 homes), compared with 2.5 per cent (463,000 homes) in 1986. Meanwhile, the number of properties that are unfit (using the most recent fitness standard) is down just a little from its 1986 figure of 1.66 million dwellings to 1.5 million today (7.6 per cent of the stock). This continues to be a worryingly high figure, although about a third of these homes could achieve fitness with expenditure of less than £500.

In summary, there are something over a million properties that remain in bad condition and need a good deal spent on them. These are occupied disproportionately by single elderly people and are older, privately rented properties.

Public expenditure constraints have led to a reduction in improvement grants to private landlords or to home owners. A number of local care and repair schemes have been established to rescue unsatisfactory houses and make them comfortable, at least for the life expectancy of the current occupier. Staying put projects of this kind help people to remain independently in their own homes, with services being brought to them, but have yet to cover the country and can make only a modest contribution at present. However, faced with tight budgets and restrictions on the spending of their capital receipts from selling council houses, local authorities have devoted the bulk of their capital spending to the renovation of existing council housing. Their work has made a huge impact on the target of £10 billion estimated by the Audit Commission, among others, to be necessary.

Local environments

It is important to note that the EHCS statistics on conditions say little about the environment in which individual properties are located. Moreover, they do not address the question of serious deterioration in the council housing sector, where some estates now offer very insecure and poor-quality environments.

An increasing trend is for residents who are better off to leave deteriorating estates – sometimes aided by cash incentives paid by the government – and this has tended to exacerbate the problems of the concentration and segregation of poorer households within particular locations. This has led to the overloading of some local services and consequent increases in crime, violence and vandalism. Such estates are becoming increasingly stigmatised, thereby reducing the life chances of people living there. In many cases, unpopular high-rise blocks, a design which precludes 'defensible space', and poor-quality building, often linked with the use of industrialised building techniques, have all combined to increase the misery of living on the worst council estates. New estates built by housing associations have replicated these problems (Page, 1993). But although poor conditions may make for a less comfortable life and greater insecurity from crime – and fear of crime – and the social disadvantages of living on a 'marginalised' estate, can these conditions be said to affect people's health?

Links between housing and health

The link between health and housing was clearer a hundred – or even fifty – years ago. The drive to replace slums with new homes was based on a recognition that more sanitary conditions would improve public health. Indeed, up to the time of the Second World War, the Minister of Health was responsible for the nation's housing. Today, following the eradication of epidemics spread by a lack of sanitation and clean water, we may not see the health and housing connections so clearly.

Two books published in 1993 – *Homes and Health* by Ineichen and *Unhealthy Housing* edited by Burridge and Ormandy – pull together an impressive array of evidence to explain how housing and health interact. In addition, *Health, Housing and Social Policy* by Arblaster and Hawtin (1993) summarises the case for reducing health inequalities by improving housing conditions. Together, these studies add up to a compelling case for accepting that 'bad housing damages your health'.

This section reviews the available evidence about housing and health. First, it considers the impact of homelessness on people's health. Secondly, it looks at the health problems caused by damp and cold housing. Next it considers how poor housing design can result in fires, accidents and infestations which damage health. It then reviews the evidence more generally about the impact of housing on individuals' mental health. Finally, it looks at the centrality of housing to the success of the care in the community policies.

Homelessness and health

Few would need convincing that the extreme conditions of homelessness, of sleeping rough, are bound to affect health. A 1989 study found that 25 per cent of the people sleeping rough and in supportive housing projects reported an in-patient hospital stay in the previous year, compared with 9 per cent of the population as a whole (Stern *et al.*, 1989). Bronchitis, tuberculosis, arthritis, skin diseases and infections, as well as alcohol/drug-related problems and psychiatric difficulties are all more prevalent among single people who are homeless (Barry *et al.*, 1991).

More recent research indicates that chronic chest conditions or breathing problems were three times as high among people sleeping rough, as in the general population; for single people in hostels and bed-and-breakfast hotels the figure was twice that of the general population. Much the same results were discovered in relation to frequent headaches, musculoskeletal problems and difficulties in seeing (although heart problems were consistently lower among people who were homeless). The study also shows that many young people recently made homeless do not have adequate access to health care. All people who are homeless are at a particular disadvantage unless special service provision is designed for them (Bines, 1994).

Families living in temporary accommodation of the bed-and-breakfast kind face a range of hazards, even if the hotel is in relatively good condition.

> *It is difficult to maintain hygiene while washing, eating and sleeping in one overcrowded room. High levels of gastroenteritis, skin disorders and chest infections have been reported. Kitchen facilities are often absent or inadequate, so people are forced to rely on foods from cafes and take-aways, which is expensive and may be nutritionally unsatisfactory. The stress of hotel life undermines parents' relationships with each other and their children. Normal child development is impaired through lack of space for safe play and exploration. High rates of accidents to children have been reported, probably due to a combination of lack of space and hazards such as kettles at floor level.*
>
> (BMA, 1987, pp. 13–14)

Cold and damp homes

Perhaps the clearest evidence that poor housing has an impact on health relates to the effects of inadequate heating and dampness.

Obviously, hypothermia is related to inadequate levels of warmth. It is clear from the higher proportion of deaths in winter than in summer (and the further increase in deaths when the winter is very cold) that many older people who die as a result of respiratory disease, heart disease or a stroke have had their illness exacerbated by the cold. A survey of older people in 1988 found that 25 per cent were not using as much heat as they would have liked because of the cost (Savage, 1988). Unmodernised older properties have far higher heating costs – mostly because of low standards of insulation – than improved and newer homes. (On a scale from 0 to 10, new homes will typically have a national home energy rating of 7–8, whereas an unmodernised Victorian house might only score 2–3 on the scale).

Dampness in the home very clearly contributes to respiratory illness.

> *The house dust mite and fungal spores both thrive in damp housing conditions. The debris of that house dust mite, particularly its faecal pellets, act as an allergen and can cause chest problems such as wheezing.*
>
> *Condensation, which is almost pure water, unlike penetrating or rising damp where the water contains salts, encourages the growth of fungal spores. These can cause allergies such as asthma, a runny nose (rhinitis), and inflammation of the lungs (alveolitis).*
>
> (Arblaster and Hawtin, 1993, p. 17)

A study in Edinburgh found that children living in homes affected by damp and mould were twice as likely to have wheezing and chesty coughs as those who slept in dry rooms. This was unrelated to smoking in the household (Strachan, 1988). In a survey of housing in Glasgow, Edinburgh and London, Platt and colleagues (1989) found higher levels of a whole range of symptoms for both children and adults in damp and mouldy houses against dry dwellings. There appeared to be a dose-response relationship, with the number of symptoms increasing with the number of housing problems. Again, the relationship was independent of smoking and socioeconomic factors.

Housing design

Forty per cent of all fatal accidents in the UK happen in the home; home-related accidents are the most common cause of death in children aged over 1 year, and almost half of all accidents to children are associated with architectural features in and around the home (DTI, 1991). Households in disadvantaged circumstances are likely to be the worst affected by such accidents (Constantinides, 1988).

Those living in high-rise buildings are more prone to serious accidents, such as falling from windows and balconies. Coroners' records for England and Wales show that in 1973–76 children living above the first floor were fifty-seven times more likely to be killed by falling than children in accommodation on the ground and first floors. Moreover, the danger of fire spreading through tower blocks is well known to fire brigades.

The Child Accident Prevention Trust has noted that families living in temporary accommodation are particularly likely to suffer accidents in the home: accommodation in bed-and-breakfast hotels and similar housing is notoriously ill designed, ill equipped and ill maintained (CAPT, 1989).

The descriptions given in Box 4.1 of system-built tower blocks – frequently constructed with low-quality materials and poor workmanship – in Belfast and Manchester could be applied in a hundred other towns and cities. The industrialised building techniques of the

Box 4.1: High-rise blocks and health

Divis Estate in Belfast

Cracks in the cladding, poorly constructed joints, ill-fitting windows, cold bridging between slabs, and poor insulation made the flats cold and damp. Flat roofs encouraged penetrating damp. Asbestos had been widely used for insulation, including blue asbestos rope around the window panels. Calcium chloride had been added to the cement to speed the drying time, and when the concrete later cracked water penetrated and chloride ions attacked the steel supporting beams. There were problems with the sewerage system, and flooding was common. Rats and cockroaches colonised cracks in the structure.

(Lowry, 1990, p. 390)

Hulme Estate in Manchester

The ducts, heated by the hot water pipes, became warm, moist environments, often contaminated with sewage, as soil pipes began to develop leaks. These conditions of high temperature and humidity are ideal for cockroach development, reproduction and movement and soon immense populations of German cockroach built up. ... The local authority was eventually forced to carry out whole-block saturation pesticide application. ...

... the health effects of this cockroach infestation ... should be considered. ... the tenants suffered the risk of pathogens carried on to food by the cockroaches. They also suffered the possibility of cockroach allergy. ... considerable stress and inconvenience and will have been subjected to pesticide exposure. ...

... a cockroach infestation which is now merely controlled, eradication not being possible, has caused, and will continue to cause, danger to the health of occupants.

(Howard, 1993, pp. 278–9)

1960s and early 1970s have left a legacy – sometimes compounded by poor maintenance – which will create problems for years to come. As well as problems of damp and condensation, which affect health, buildings of this kind are particularly prone to infestation by cockroaches, which thrive in warm wet conditions. The risk to tenants from such infestation comes from germs transferred from house to house, from allergy (caused by the bodies of dead cockroaches remaining in ducting), from the use of pesticides to kill the cockroaches, and from stress caused by the infestation (Freeman, 1993).

Housing and stress

Statistics are less helpful in establishing a clear link between housing and stress-related illness. Nevertheless, there are good grounds for believing that poor sound insulation between neighbouring homes, a lack of privacy and overcrowding are all likely to contribute to mental health problems. In an analysis of housing and health in Edinburgh, Glasgow and London, Hunt (1990) found that indicators of emotional stress were much more common for both adults and children in the presence of adverse housing conditions.

Since women spend more time in the home, bad housing affects them to a greater degree. Interviews with women over many years have noted the relationship between their mental health and overcrowding, neighbourhood noise and poor structural conditions (Gabe and Williams, 1993). Although there is evidence of a strong association, it is impossible to say whether it is causal. It may be other factors that cause the stress rather than the housing conditions *per se*. For example, poor housing conditions are much more prevalent among groups with low incomes (Hills, 1993).

Care in the home

The government white paper, *Caring for People,* acknowledged that 'housing is a vital component of community care and it is often the key to independent living' (Cm 849, 1989, p. 25). But there is considerable room for improvement. Policies for care in the community depend upon suitable home environments. Here the connection between health and housing relates to the role of the home in contributing to recovery. Much more than ever before, people with health problems are expected to live and be cared for in their homes. This might be an older person being discharged from hospital much earlier than in the past, or the integration in the community of someone leaving a psychiatric hospital, or the result of a general policy to keep people out of residential care and other institutions. Such changes in policy require adequate housing in the community.

Unfortunately, as the *English House Condition Survey 1991* (DoE, 1993) shows, many unsatisfactory properties are not owned by disreputable absentee landlords but are in the owner-occupied sector. Often the owners are older people who find it difficult to cope with the management and maintenance of their property, let alone its full-scale modernisation, and so conditions can deteriorate. Yet policies for community care are predicated on the expectation that care users are living in satisfactory homes.

Overview

Sifting the evidence, and especially extracting the effects of bad housing from other determinants of poor health, is not an easy exercise. But the literature now demonstrates beyond doubt that the connection is real: bad housing is dangerous to your health. Tackling housing problems should therefore reduce inequalities in health. The remainder of this chapter considers how this might be done.

The policy context

Before launching into a 'wish list' of housing policies, the realities of public expenditure constraints must be accepted. What would increased expenditure on housing do to the rest of the economy? How much can the nation afford to devote to easing housing problems? First, the section considers the level of public expenditure devoted to housing. It then reviews how public money is spent on housing in terms of subsidies to home owners and the provision of social housing. It discusses the policy changes required in both of these areas to remove inequalities and expand the number of homes available. Finally, it examines the role of the housing sector in stimulating the economy as a whole.

Investment in housing

During the 1990s the government deficit in the UK has risen relative to those of other European countries (OECD, 1992). Efforts to curb public expenditure have led to further cuts in the capital budget for housing. As Figure 4.3 shows, in contrast to spending on health, social security, personal social services, law and order etc., housing had already suffered a sharp decline over the previous decade. Moreover, the sale of council houses has been contributing very substantial sums to ease the government's funding problems. So far, sales have returned some £47 billion, which compares with £60 billion for the proceeds of privatisation from all sources put together. Housing, therefore, has been disproportionately taking the strain at a time of restraint on the public sector borrowing requirement (PSBR) (Wilcox, 1993a; 1994a).

In the 1993 consolidated autumn statement the government announced further reductions in spending by local authorities and, in particular, by housing associations. The associations will see £575 million cut from their programme of funding from the Housing Corporation over the next two years, and this will lead to a fall in their output of rented homes from over 50,000 per annum to under 30,000. A side effect of these reductions is the loss of jobs in the construction industry.

Subsidies to home owners

In the 1993 budget the Chancellor also announced further reductions in the level of mortgage interest tax relief for home owners. Instead of allowing relief at 25p in the pound,

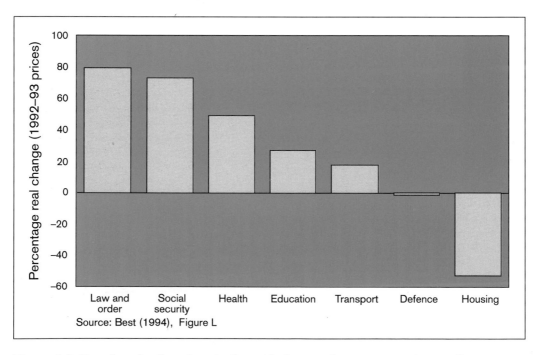

Figure 4.3: Housing declines in priority, real changes in government spending, 1980–81 to 1993–94

the figure was reduced to 20p in 1994–95 and will go down in 1995–96 to 15p. This will achieve savings for the Exchequer of some £600 million per annum, compared with the level prevailing in 1993–94.

The *Inquiry into British Housing* chaired by the Duke of Edinburgh, which produced its first report in 1985 (National Federation of Housing Associations, 1985) and its second in 1991 (Joseph Rowntree Foundation, 1991), was keen to see a phasing-out of tax relief on mortgages, as it created an 'uneven playing field' between renting and owning and provided support disproportionately to those who were better off. However, the *Inquiry* believed that the savings achieved should be recycled to ease acute housing problems, going first to finance personal subsidies to cover mortgage costs (mortgage benefit, similar to housing benefit), creating a 'needs-related housing allowance' which would also be available to poorer owner occupiers who are struggling with the maintenance costs for their home (Joseph Rowntree Foundation, 1991).

Mortgage benefit would provide the safety net for owners who are hit by a change of circumstance, such as the rapid increases in interest rates at the beginning of the 1990s, or the loss of employment by one partner in a household. The absence of targeted financial support in these circumstances reveals a major flaw in the policies of the 1980s that promoted home ownership so heavily (Wilcox, 1993a). Indeed, the growth of repossessions and mortgage arrears, shown in Figure 4.4, has produced the most startling changes in the housing scene over recent years.

Helping less fortunate home owners would not absorb all the savings from phasing out tax

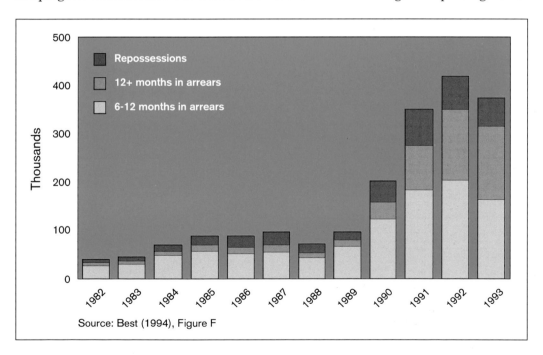

Figure 4.4: **Mortgage arrears and repossessions, Great Britain, 1982–93**

relief. The *Inquiry* believed the remainder should go to boosting the quantity and quality of rented housing, both through modest tax concessions to stimulate the private sector and through direct support to the housing associations and local authority landlords.

Raising finance for social housing

The reduction in the role of council housing has been driven partly by hopes of a more competitive, market-orientated system. As a result, housing associations have been propelled into the position previously occupied by local authority housing departments. The public investment in housing associations has been stretched by reductions in the levels of grant paid for each extra home, leaving associations to borrow the balance from the private sector and repay these loans out of rents. Although this has achieved a competitive framework for the provision of social housing – with associations vying for the public money – it has led to much higher rents, which have, in turn, created the poverty trap of reliance on benefits, with strong disincentives to work, or to work harder, as discussed below.

Nevertheless, because housing associations are deemed to lie outside the public sector, the money they spend is not counted within the PSBR when they borrow from private sources. Thus if a housing association builds a new home, only the grant element – often around half the total – counts as public spending, whereas if the same home were provided by a local authority, 100 per cent of its costs would be regarded as public expenditure.

These accounting conventions have stimulated greater interest in the idea of local authorities passing their properties out of direct ownership into the hands of newly created organisations (often using the same staff). Such voluntary transfers have now shifted over 150,000 homes out of the public sector. This trend seems likely to continue, and may generate the extra resources which are so badly needed to rectify deficiencies in local authority stock. Valued conservatively at £40 billion, the outstanding debt on council housing is only about half this figure, so if the properties were in the hands of a housing association – or a local housing company, as suggested in a joint publication by the Joseph Rowntree Foundation and the Institute of Housing – a further £20 billion could be borrowed against these assets. This would provide the investment needed to renew the worst estates and improve their environments without any consequences for public expenditure totals (Wilcox *et al.*, 1993).

Housing and the national economy

Finally, there are the implications of housing investment on the wider economy and the nation's overall prosperity.

Work for the Joseph Rowntree Foundation by Geoff Meen at Oxford Forecasting Centre has shown how extra capital spending on housing of £1 billion could increase the numbers of people employed in construction and related industries, at a net cost (after receipt of tax, rental returns etc.) of approximately half a billion pounds in the following year. At a time of much anxiety at the continuing loss of full-time employment, particularly in manual occupations, such investment has an important social spin-off (Meen, 1993).

Investment in rented housing, following the demise of the business expansion scheme arrangements, which have proved useful but expensive, would assist those who need to move for job reasons but are currently tied down by the lack of alternatives to home ownership. Younger, more affluent people need the opportunity for mobility that the private sector can bring. Providing incentives for private renting can be offset by the gains from the same households not claiming tax relief as home owners.

Providing bricks-and-mortar grants to keep rents within the reach of those in low-paid employment, without forcing them into reliance on housing benefit, also has important effects on the national economy. Cutting the producer subsidies and raising rents is inflationary and counter-productive (Meen, 1994).

Two-thirds of those in housing association and local authority homes already get housing benefit, so the substantial increases in their rents over recent years has simply meant the money going round in a circle (with high administrative costs in the middle). Over recent years rents have risen at a far higher rate than earnings: this is inflationary, encourages wage claims at high levels, which hinders international competitiveness, and leads indirectly to higher government pay-outs on benefits linked to the retail price index (because rent levels are taken into account in its calculation). Paradoxically, higher rents, resulting from lower grants to providers, can end up costing the government more (Meen, 1994).

In addition, when rents pass the point at which households have to accept housing benefit, incentives to earn more are substantially reduced. Figure 4.5 shows how little is gained by a family with low wages as a combination of family credit, free school meals, council tax

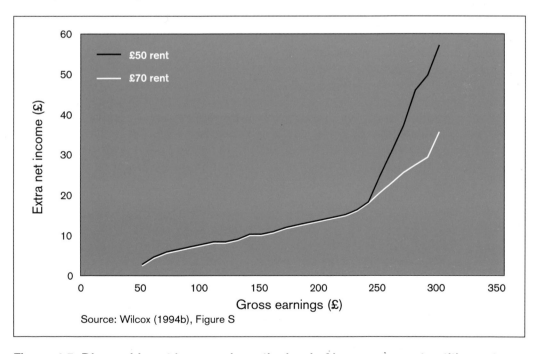

Source: Wilcox (1994b), Figure S

Figure 4.5: Disposable net income above the level of income support entitlement – family with two children

and housing benefit is withdrawn, as earnings rise from £50 per week to £230 per week. A couple with two children would have to earn £270 per week to be just £30 better off than earning £80 with a rent of £50 per week; if their rent was £70 per week they would have to earn over £300 to achieve this net gain in income (Wilcox, 1994b). These figures make no allowance for work-related costs such as travel or childcare. High rents, therefore, present fierce disincentives for many to obtain employment, and for others to do overtime (or for two partners both to work). The lone mother must earn more than average female manual earnings to escape the housing benefit poverty trap if the rent is at the average level for new housing association homes (Wilcox, 1993b). Yet staying at home, unable to improve one's standard of living by working, undermines self-respect.

Overview

The research summarised above has indicated how the recycling of current resources could finance the support needed by home owners who face difficulty in meeting their mortgage commitments, and the private and social landlords who could be supported to expand their output. The effect of retargeting tax relief to individuals, refinancing public sector housing outside the constraints of the PSBR, and expanding the provision of rented homes with support to the producers, would contribute to a healthier and more competitive economy.

The remedies

Given that funding for housing solutions is not as problematic as it might appear, what specific measures could have the most favourable impact on the health of the nation? Discussions at the Ditchley Park seminar identified three areas of opportunity for improving health through better housing.

Investment in new and improved housing

Targeted investment in new and improved housing would improve health by reducing the risks of accident and fire, as well as overcrowding and cold, damp conditions. Without the need for homeless families to live in substandard bed-and-breakfast hotels, not only would fire and safety hazards be reduced but, in the longer term, public money would be saved.

As noted above, more and better housing could be provided if existing housing subsidies were spent to greater effect. Subsidies to owner occupiers through mortgage interest tax relief are now being curtailed and could be redirected, both through targeting on home owners in need and through stimulating the production of affordable, good-quality homes for rent. Furthermore, borrowing against the hidden assets in the council sector could unlock the resources to tackle the disrepair on council estates.

It is equally possible to envisage adequate funding to improve substandard owner-occupied housing, where often the home owner is an older person. Frequently there is equity tied up in the home (since mortgages have been repaid) which could be released to finance building works. Sometimes a service of advice and information, provided through care and repair agencies or the local authority, may make a major difference in encouraging anxious owners to get much-needed work done to their home. Higher levels of improvement grant are not the only answer here (Leather and Mackintosh, 1994).

Heating and insulation

In trying to maximise value for money, spending on better insulation and heating systems (combined with adequate ventilation) may give the best returns. Not only does the consequent reduction in cold and damp improve health, but it also reduces fuel bills (Markus, 1993), which are of particular importance now that VAT has been added to home energy costs. In rented property landlords also gain from the lower maintenance costs that follow from reductions in condensation, mould growth and the deteriorating effects of dampness. At the same time, expenditure here has global benefits by reducing emissions of CO_2 (greenhouse) gases (Haylock, 1993).

Investment in disadvantaged neighbourhoods

The determinants of health include the social and community networks that surround the individual. Strengthening such networks can provide emotional support, which reduces stress and alleviates isolation. In turn, this can improve the health of people in disadvantaged circumstances.

Investment in community development – paying for common facilities, funding individuals on estates who can co-ordinate activities, as well as securing environmental improvements – can reduce crime/fear of crime, stress and mental illness. Supervised play facilities can allow children to take exercise in safety, thereby reducing accidents. If the physical regeneration of an area involves the residents the gains are multiplied: employment is generated, there are opportunities for training in new skills, and the capacity of those in disadvantaged neighbourhoods is enhanced. The marked improvement that follows from community-led development is illustrated on the Meadowell estate in North Tyneside (Gibson, 1993). A recent review of experiences in eight cities in the UK and Germany shows how the improvement of multiply deprived neighbourhoods must integrate physical and economic initiatives with social renewal (Thake and Staubach, 1993).

Investment in disadvantaged neighbourhoods can also tackle the deterioration in quality of life that follows from the concentration and segregation of poorer households. Neighbourhoods, and individual new estates, need some mix of people in employment alongside those who are unemployed; of households without children as well as those with children (reducing overall child density); of home owners (or shared owners) among properties for rent; and of different age groups. This balance of income groups, tenures and ages can prevent the creation of 'welfare housing', where an inevitable overload on services follows from the concentration and isolation of those suffering the greatest disadvantages. The ghettos of American cities – characterised by 'wave upon wave of violence and crime' – provide stark evidence of what happens when public housing becomes the 'housing of last resort' and areas face a breakdown of normal social controls (Carr, 1993; Kasarda, 1993; Newman, 1993).

Avoiding the poverty trap

An insidious new dimension to housing problems relates to the cost of accommodation, which falls upon those with lower incomes. Building new homes and improving existing housing will not solve the difficulties faced by poorer households if they cannot afford to live in these houses. There are two important dimensions to this: mortgage benefits and increased capital subsidies to the providers of social housing.

Mortgage benefits, as discussed above, should be introduced to provide a much-needed safety net for owner occupiers with low wages who have problems meeting repayments, because of reduced income in a recession, loss of employment of a member of the household or high interest rates. Mortgage benefits could help to counter the exponential rise in mortgage arrears and repossessions that occurred in the 1980s (see Figure 4.4, p. 63).

Capital subsidies to the providers of social housing – principally to local authorities in the past and to housing associations today – should be increased. This can reduce the price of a home, allowing the landlord to charge a rent which does not automatically impoverish the tenant or drive them into dependency on benefits. Such subsidies have been out of favour in recent years, but the concentration on personal subsidies to the individual – housing benefit – has distinct disadvantages, as highlighted above. Enabling rents to be lowered by increasing capital subsidies to providers would remove the disincentives for individuals to take up low-wage employment, without a substantial increase in government expenditure because of the resulting reduction in housing benefits. Availability of housing, therefore, is not the only consideration: decent homes must also be affordable.

Conclusion

Tackling inequalities in housing also addresses health inequalities. National investment in new and improved housing, and in improving disadvantaged neighbourhoods, also has important impacts on the wider issues of health and wellbeing. Thus, heavy expenditure on reducing cold and damp conditions on a council estate will not only reduce illness among the residents but can also be the catalyst for community development – the involvement of residents in the whole process – as well as bringing the opportunity for jobs and skill-building to the estate, with spin-offs in reducing the crime and stress associated with poverty.

Good housing and good health go together: the health of the nation depends on recognising this connection.

CHAPTER **5**

Family poverty and poor health

Michaela Benzeval and Steven Webb

Introduction

The primary focus of this chapter is the link between family poverty and poor health. It is important to be clear, however, that the intention is to look specifically at the problems associated with low incomes rather than the broader notion of deprivation (P. Townsend, 1987). Although there is a considerable British literature demonstrating the association between various measures of socioeconomic status or deprivation and health, there is relatively little evidence based on income *per se*. However, international evidence does exist that clearly shows the strong link between low income and poor health outcomes.

The purpose of this chapter is to assess what changes might be made to public policy to relieve poverty and thereby to improve health outcomes, particularly among families with children. The chapter begins, however, with a brief description of the current pattern and causes of family poverty in the UK. It then surveys the empirical evidence available on the link between low income and poor health. Finally, it describes and evaluates a range of policy measures designed to tackle family poverty in ways that might be expected to reduce existing health inequalities.

Which families are poor?

The best source of official statistics on low incomes in Britain is the Department of Social Security's publication *Households Below Average Income* (HBAI). The latest edition covers the period 1979–1991/92 (DSS, 1994a) and gives details of the number and characteristics of individuals who are members of households with incomes below various fractions of the national average. Some of the key methodological assumptions of the HBAI analysis are shown in Box 5.1.

The HBAI statistics do not provide a single 'poverty line', but rather give statistics for the size and composition of groups below various income thresholds. This approach is quite helpful, given that the use of a single 'poverty line' can sometimes give misleading results.

Box 5.1: Households below average income: methodological assumptions

There are two main features of the HBAI statistics which should be noted.

1 Living standards are assessed in terms of the income of a complete household, and all household members are assumed to enjoy the same living standard. Clearly, this assumption could lead to an understatement of poverty where resources are not adequately shared within the household. Indeed, in the context of the health implications of low incomes, a crucial factor may well be the proportion of household income going to the mother rather than simply the total household income (see, for example, Graham, 1984).

2 Household incomes are adjusted to reflect differences in household size and composition by means of an 'equivalence scale'. For example, a single person is deemed to need around 60 per cent of the income of a childless couple to attain the same living standard, whereas a couple with two primary school children is deemed to need around 144 per cent of the income of a childless couple to attain a given standard of living. Clearly, the resulting income estimates are somewhat sensitive to the specific assumptions made about the relative needs of families with and without children, particularly among the poorest groups.

Table 5.1 presents the DSS figures for the number of individuals with household incomes below various thresholds, classified by broad family type. (A time series of HBAI analyses for 1961–91 can be found in Goodman and Webb, 1994.) It should be noted that the columns are cumulative so that, for example, all those included in the less than 40 per cent column are also included in the subsequent columns. Figure 5.1 highlights the distribution of family types in the poorest group – below 40 per cent of average income.

Table 5.1: Individuals with household income[1] below various proportions of the UK average in 1991–92, in millions

Family type	Less than 40 per cent	Less than 50 per cent	Less than 60 per cent	Whole population
Couples with children	3.5	5.2	6.9	21.6
Lone parents with children	1.0	2.1	2.5	3.6
Pensioners	1.1	3.2	4.4	9.7
Other without children	2.3	3.5	4.5	21.6
Total[2]	7.9	13.9	18.4	56.6

Notes:
1. Income is after housing costs
2. Columns do not always add up to total because of rounding

Source: Derived from DSS (1994a), Table B1; Table F1(AHC)

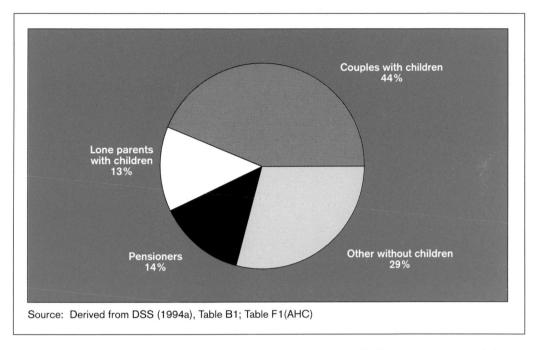

Source: Derived from DSS (1994a), Table B1; Table F1(AHC)

Figure 5.1: Individuals with equivalised household income below 40 per cent of the UK average in 1991–92, n = 7.9 million

Table 5.1 and Figure 5.1 show that families with children – both couples and lone parents – are over-represented at the bottom end of the income distribution. They form 4.5 million out of 7.9 million, or 57 per cent, of the poorest group with less than 40 per cent of average household income, but comprise only 45 per cent of the population. If the poverty line is drawn rather higher – for example at 60 per cent of average income – then families with children are still over-represented but the pattern is much less marked. In other words, families with children are more likely than other groups to be poor, and are particularly likely to have very low incomes.

Although Table 5.1 gives results for the aggregate incidence of low incomes among families with children, it does not provide much insight into the causes of poverty. A better guide is given in Table 5.2, which focuses exclusively on dependent children in households with low incomes. The classification in the table is by the marital status of the parent(s) and their economic position – distinguishing between families with no full-time worker, at least one full-time employee or a self-employed worker.

A number of causes of low income may be inferred from Table 5.2.

1 *Unemployment:* many of those in the category – no full-time worker, couples with children – will be the children of people who are unemployed; although they only make up one in seven of all children, they comprise almost half of the poorest group.

2 *Lone parenthood:* very few lone parents are able to combine full-time work with childcare responsibilities, and so around three-quarters are in receipt of income support; around

71

Table 5.2: Dependent children with household income[1] below various proportions of the UK average in 1991–92, in millions

Family type	Less than 40 per cent	Less than 50 per cent	Less than 60 per cent	Whole population
No full-time worker				
– lone parents	0.7	1.3	1.5	1.8
– couples with children	1.2	1.4	1.6	1.9
One or more full-time workers				
– 1 or 2 children	0.2	0.4	0.8	5.3
– 3 or more children	0.1	0.4	0.6	2.0
Self-employed	0.4	0.5	0.6	1.7
Total[2]	2.5	4.1	5.2	12.7

Notes:
1. Income is after housing costs
2. Columns do not always add up to total because of rounding

Source: Derived from DSS (1994a), Table B3; Table F3(AHC)

one and a half million children of lone parents are in households with incomes below 60 per cent of the national average.

3 *Low wages/high outgoings:* around a third of a million children in families where there is a full-time employee (defined as thirty hours per week or more) are in the lowest income category. One of the main factors here is the lack of social security to assist with the mortgage costs of full-timers (Webb and Wilcox, 1991); when interest rates touch 15 per cent, as they did in the early 1990s, this can put severe pressure on disposable incomes.

4 *Self-employment:* the figures would seem to suggest that the children of the self-employed are particularly vulnerable to extremes of low income. There is, however, some uncertainty about the reliability of these figures as a guide to the living standards of the self-employed, particularly since the expenditure levels of many of these apparently poor households are relatively high.

Families with children form a disproportionate part of the poorest section of society. This is particularly true of lone-parent families and the families of people who are unemployed or earn low wages. The next section considers what impact this has on their health.

The link between family poverty and poor health

As highlighted in Chapter 2, numerous studies over the last century in Britain have demonstrated an association between disadvantaged socioeconomic status, however measured, and poor health outcomes. One implication of these analyses is that one would expect low income to be associated with poor health. This is in fact the case, although there are relatively few British studies that document the links between income and health in a very convincing fashion. Fortunately, there is a solid body of international evidence available with which to supplement British data. This section therefore begins by examining the international evidence and then reports the available evidence from Britain in a little more detail. Finally, it reviews how income might have an impact on poor health.

International evidence

Evidence from Europe, North America and Australia demonstrates a strong negative association between income on the one hand, and mortality, life expectancy and morbidity on the other.

As far as Europe is concerned, Blaxter (1989) reports higher rates of chronic illness in France, Norway and Finland among people with low rather than high incomes. Similarly, Reijneveld and Gunning-Schepers (1994) have demonstrated a strong negative correlation between average income and standardised mortality ratios in the boroughs in Amsterdam, and Elmén (1993) found that the relative risk of infant mortality was twice as high in areas with low rather than high income in Göteburg, Sweden. A more detailed study has been conducted in Finland where the 1980 census records were linked to the death certificates of all individuals who died between 1981 and 1985. In an analysis of people aged over 65, Martelin (1994) found that men in the lowest income quartile (defined as family disposable income per consumption unit) were 28 per cent more likely to die having controlled for age, and 16 per cent more likely to die when other socioeconomic factors were taken into account, than those in the highest quartile. For women, the mortality differentials were 31 per cent and 12 per cent respectively.

In the USA, the first major study of income and health matched census information and death certificates for a sample of people who died between May and August 1960. Controlling for age, Kitagawa and Hauser (1973) found higher mortality rates among black and white, men and women, with low incomes. Pappas and colleagues (1993) replicated the 1973 analysis by combining data from the 1986 *National Health Interview Survey* and the *National Mortality Followback Survey*. White men with an annual family income of less than $10,000 had a death rate seven times higher than those with an income greater than $25,000. The differential was fourfold for white women, fivefold for black men and threefold for black women. Comparing the results with those of Kitagawa and Hauser, Pappas and colleagues found that 'from 1960 through 1986, the differences in mortality widened between income groups' (1993, p. 106).

The *National Health Interview Survey* in the USA has also been used to examine the relationship between family income and morbidity. Using 1988 data, Rice (1991) found that five times as many people with a family income less than $10,000 reported their health as only fair or poor, as individuals with incomes greater than $35,000. At least three times as many people in the lowest income group reported that their activities were limited due to chronic illness, as those in the highest group.

In Canada, men in the highest quartile of the income distribution can expect to live 6.3 years longer, and 14.3 more years free of disability, than those in the lowest quartile. For women the differences are 3 and 7.6 years respectively (Robine and Ritchie, 1991).

Probably the most comprehensive analysis of income and morbidity to date was conducted in Australia (National Health Strategy, 1992). Using the *National Health Survey* for 1989–90, equivalised income was calculated for all survey respondents and compared to a range of morbidity measures. In the lowest income quintile, men were 167 per cent (women 148 per cent) more likely to report their health as fair or poor and 138 per cent (women 83 per cent) more likely to suffer a disability than those in the highest income quintile. In a multivariate analysis that controlled for demographic, socioeconomic and behavioural risk factors, equivalised income remained statistically significant for a range of health measures. For example, boys under 15 in the lowest income quintile were 45 per cent (girls 31 per cent) more likely to have a chronic illness than those in the highest.

British evidence

Two main national British surveys have contained information on both income and health: the *Health and Lifestyle Survey* (HALS) and the *General Household Survey* (GHS). Evidence from each will be summarised in turn.

HALS contains information about 9,000 people for a wide range of health variables and a rather crude measure of household income. Nevertheless, Blaxter (1990) found a clear and consistent association between income and health: groups with low incomes reported the highest rates of morbidity and disability. Indeed, in a multivariate analysis of the relative importance of income and social class, she argues that 'the apparently strong association of social class and health is primarily an association of income and health' (p. 72). In a more specific analysis of HALS data focusing on back pain, Croft and Rigby (1994) found that after controlling for age, women with a monthly household income of less than £230 were over one and a half times more likely to report back pain than women with an income greater than £996 per month.

The first analysis of income and health using the GHS was based on the 1976 data. Hurst (1985) found that 'limiting long-standing illness is over twice as high for the first decile [lowest] and over three times as high for the second decile as for the tenth decile [highest]' (p. 114). Despite the crudeness of this analysis – the health measure did not control for age and sex, or the income measure for family structure – it clearly showed the higher levels of illness among groups with low incomes. Subsequently, O'Donnell and Propper (1991) took both of the factors neglected by Hurst into account when they analysed the 1985 GHS. Figure 5.2 illustrates their results for two measures of morbidity. Using quintiles of equivalent income they found a statistically significant negative relationship between income and age/sex-standardised morbidity. The inequality was greatest for subjective assessments of health: 9 per cent of people reporting their health as not good were in the highest quintile and 35 per cent were in the poorest quintile against 20 per cent of the population in each group.

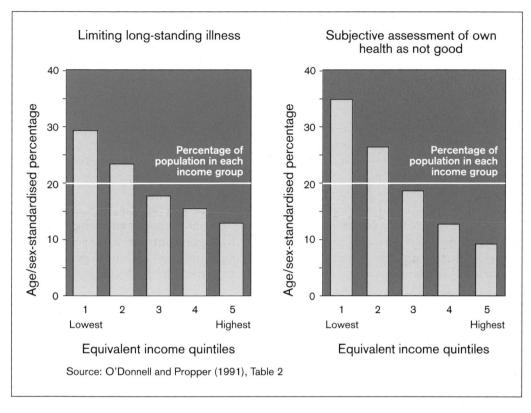

Figure 5.2: Age/sex-standardised numbers of individuals reporting morbidity in each equivalent income group as a percentage of all individuals reporting morbidity, *General Household Survey,* Great Britain, 1985

Evidence that low incomes are independently associated with poor health appears convincing. However, in designing policies aimed at countering poor health outcomes among families with low incomes it is important to consider how lack of income may have an adverse effect on health. There are two related but distinct accounts in the existing literature. The first examines how poverty might affect health and the second focuses on the effects of income inequality in society as a whole. We consider each in turn.

How low income affects health

Blackburn (1991) suggests that three distinct but interacting processes are important in considering the way low income may have an impact on family health: physiological, psychological and behavioural.

Physiological

Income provides the means of obtaining the fundamental prerequisites for health, such as shelter, food, warmth and the ability to participate in society. Low income, therefore, increases individuals' exposure to harmful environments, such as inadequate housing;

reduces a family's ability to purchase necessities such as a healthy diet; and increases stresses as families struggle to cope with small budgets.

For example, an analysis of the 1986 *English House Conditions Survey* by the Department of Social Security (DSS, 1993) showed that the poorest quarter of the population was more likely to live in accommodation which was 'unfit', 'lacking basic amenities' or in 'poor repair' than the rest of the population. As shown in Chapter 4, such poor housing conditions can have a detrimental effect on health. Similarly, Blackburn (1991) reports an analysis of the *National Food Survey* which indicated that families with low incomes have a lower intake of nearly all nutrients than those whose incomes are high. A study by the National Children's Home (NCH) (1991) found that even very young children in households with low incomes sometimes go without food for lack of money.

Psychological

Living with limited access to resources creates stresses and reduces individuals' ability, choices and support to solve problems. Stress and poor social support have been shown to have a detrimental effect on health. For example, parenting on low incomes has been shown to be associated with stress and depression among women (Brown and Harris, 1978).

Behavioural

Poverty may result in health-damaging behaviours that affect health in two principal ways. First, health-damaging behaviours – such as smoking and giving children sweets – may enable people to cope in difficult circumstances. For example, studies suggest that high smoking prevalences among people with low incomes are a 'way of meeting rather than shirking responsibility ... [providing] a way of coping with the constant and unremitting demands of caring' (Graham, 1993a, p. 182). Secondly, poverty reduces individuals' choices. For example, a study by NCH (1991) calculated that a 'healthy' diet cost 17 per cent more than an 'unhealthy' one. Blackburn (1991) argues that current benefit rates cover only 86 per cent of the nutritional needs of a 5-year-old and 68 per cent of those of an 8-year-old. Where money is scarce it may also be that families buy foods which are high in calories but low in nutrition, simply to satisfy their appetites (Leather, 1992).

These studies and many others of a similar nature would seem to support the view that a family with a very low income may have difficulty in meeting the cost of basic necessities such as food, fuel and adequate shelter, and that limited access to such necessities would be bound to have a detrimental impact on family health. Equally importantly, however, is the stress associated with coping on a low income. In addition, poverty is associated with poor social relations and unhealthy behaviours, all of which have been shown to cause poor health outcomes.

Income inequality

If poor health outcomes were wholly a consequence of absolute material deprivation, we would expect that, other things being equal, richer societies would have better health outcomes than poorer societies. However, Wilkinson (1993) has pointed out that, although in less developed countries there is a strong relationship between average per capita income and life expectancy, between developed countries this relationship is much weaker. Rather, he argues, the key determinant of the health of a developed economy is the extent of income inequality. Specifically, the more unequal the income distribution, the worse the general level of public health. Wilkinson writes:

Sweden, Norway, The Netherlands have high life expectancy and more egalitarian income distributions; West Germany, USA and the UK have less good mortality and are less egalitarian. … Japan now has the highest life expectancy in the world and the narrowest income distribution of any developed country.

(1993, p. 7)

Clearly, international comparisons of this sort are fraught with difficulty, and the other things being equal qualification is of particular importance. For example, countries with more equal income distributions may also devote more resources to public policies which benefit health. However, the relative importance of these different factors has not been investigated, and so an assessment cannot be made about the validity of this concern.

If income inequality rather than low income *per se* is a key determinant of the public health, what might be the nature of the causal relationship? Wilkinson argues that the direct physical effects of poverty are less important than the psychosocial consequences 'in terms of stress, self-esteem and social relations' (1992, p. 168).

The statistical associations between high income inequality and poorer health outcomes reported by Wilkinson are striking. Whether these relationships are causal, however, is far less clear. In other words, although inequalities in society may tend to be associated with poorer health, it does not necessarily follow that reducing income inequalities by, for example, more redistributive taxation, would automatically improve health outcomes or reduce inequalities in health. Nonetheless, Wilkinson's work does suggest that, in framing policy responses, it would be unwise to focus exclusively on the absolute living conditions of the families in the poorest circumstances.

Alleviating and preventing poverty among families

In considering possible policy responses to the problem of family poverty, it is useful to distinguish between measures that tackle the *causes* of poverty and those that merely relieve its *consequences*. When thinking about low incomes, an instinctive response is to turn immediately to the social security system and to advocate a general raising of benefit levels. But although benefit levels are important, the social security system can at best only relieve the consequences of poverty. Indeed, raising benefits can in some cases actually make it harder to escape from dependency. A better approach is to take measures that will prevent families from falling into poverty in the first place. Dealing with the causes of poverty is both better for the family concerned and in the long run makes economic sense.

In the light of this distinction, and building on debate at Ditchley Park, the remainder of this section looks first at measures to prevent poverty, next at benefit reforms to help those who remain dependent on social security, and finally at changes to the tax system that would reduce inequality and which could also finance these and other desirable reforms.

What will be clear from the foregoing description of family poverty is that the surest way to escape it is to have a well-paid job. The poverty of people who are unemployed, low paid or lone parents is clearly linked to the absence of secure employment with decent wages. Thus a first priority would be for measures to increase opportunities for training and employment, perhaps focusing specifically on people in long-term unemployment who might otherwise be most prone to experience some form of social exclusion.

A related policy would be to reduce the barriers to employment faced by groups such as lone parents. In this area the availability of good-quality affordable childcare is likely to be crucially important. At present the combination of benefit withdrawal and the costs of childcare may mean that a lone parent would actually be financially worse off taking a part-time job. Possible policy responses here include greater availability of subsidised childcare places and/or allowing childcare expenditure to be offset against income before benefit entitlement is calculated. The November 1993 budget announcement of a £40 per week childcare 'disregard' within the family credit system is consistent with the latter approach.

Any serious attempt to tackle poverty and deprivation in Britain will require a wide range of radical social policy interventions. Chapter 8 emphasises the particular need to develop new policies to widen access to childcare, education and employment. However, although enabling poorer families to obtain an income through the labour market may be seen as the most preferred option, it is unlikely that public policy will eliminate the need for a large number of families with children to depend upon the social security system in the foreseeable future. Against this background it is also helpful to consider ways in which the benefit system itself might be reformed to reduce family poverty.

Perhaps the most obvious response to the problems of material deprivation would simply be to increase benefit levels, with particular emphasis on those related to children. One aspect of such a strategy should be for the government to make a serious attempt at assessing what a minimum acceptable income would be for families of different compositions, and then to see whether and to what extent existing benefit levels enable families to reach that standard. Studies of this sort by the Family Budget Unit (Bradshaw *et al.*, 1992) have suggested that present income support levels for a two-parent household with children are about one-third below that required to attain even a 'low-cost' budget.

A strategy of increasing benefit levels for families could take various forms. One would be to increase the universal child benefit substantially above its April 1994 level of £10.20 per week for a first child and £8.25 for any other child. This approach has many attractions, including the fact that child benefit is typically paid directly to mothers, and also that its take-up rate is likely to be close to 100 per cent.

The principal drawback is inevitably that of cost. As a guide, the gross annual cost of an extra £1 per week for each of twelve million children would be roughly £600 million. Therefore, a significant increase in child benefit could cost several billion pounds. Given that a programme aiming to relieve family poverty would be likely to have other elements involving additional public spending, it seems likely that substantial increases in child benefit may not be feasible.

An alternative approach would be to channel available resources through benefits aimed specifically at families with low incomes, namely income support and family credit. This

78

approach has the potential to make a much more significant dent in the problem of family poverty. Very broadly, £1 per week for each of the twelve million children receiving child benefit would cost the same as £4 per week to each of the three million children in families receiving income support.

However, relying on the means-tested benefit system to target families in poverty is itself not without problems. In the first place there is the well-known problem of families who do not take up their entitlement to income support. The latest DSS figures (1994b) suggest that couples with children fail to take up roughly one pound in ten of their income support entitlement. The statistics do, however, show that it is typically smaller amounts that go unclaimed, and so arguably a substantial increase in the rates of benefit payable might simultaneously reduce levels of non-take-up.

A second problem with using the means-tested benefit system is its effect on the work incentives of recipients. We have already noted that the best outcome would be for a given individual to have a well-paid job rather than be dependent on benefits, and it is important that any increases in benefit levels do not make that transition more difficult. Significantly increasing income support levels would make part-time work in particular less attractive, since benefit would be withdrawn more or less pound-for-pound over a still wider range of earnings. One response that might diminish this problem would be a corresponding increase in the rates of family credit, which exists to top up the wages of workers with low pay with children.

Apart from general benefit levels, there are a number of other aspects of the social security system that might be singled out for attention with a view to improving health outcomes. One would be a reform to the social fund. At present this provides interest-free loans for the purchase of basic durables such as cookers, fridges and beds. A return to a system of grants for a limited list of basic items might relieve the pressure on the poorest households.

A related problem for poorer households is meeting bills for gas, electricity and water. Although official disconnections of gas and electricity supply have been on the decline in recent years, these have been replaced in some cases by customers effectively disconnecting themselves because of having no money for the meter. This problem is likely to worsen since the imposition of VAT on domestic fuel, particularly for families with children. Crawford and colleagues (1993) have shown how the proposed compensation package should be revised to deal with this problem adequately. Similarly, the whole issue of water charging is likely to be increasingly controversial as the water industry is forced to move away from the existing system of water rates by the year 2000, and as the real level of charges rises, in part to meet the higher environmental standards being imposed on the water companies. A co-ordinated approach is needed to the whole issue of ensuring that all households have access to basic necessities such as fuel and water.

Although much of the foregoing has concentrated on measures to improve the opportunities of those out of paid employment and to reform the benefits system, little has so far been said about the wider issue of income inequality. If, as Wilkinson has argued, income inequality is a crucial determinant of public health, then measures to reduce it should also form part of an overall package. If not, the measures listed above would still have to be paid for, and we would presumably seek to do this in ways which did not hit the incomes of people already living in poverty.

The most obvious way to reduce income inequality would be through the tax system. Income inequality has grown greatly during the 1980s in the UK and a large part of this has been due to discretionary changes to the tax and benefit structure (Johnson and Webb, 1993). The major change has been a switch from taxes on income to taxes on spending. The standard rate of income tax has been cut from 33 per cent to 25 per cent, and the highest rate on earned income has fallen from 83 per cent to 40 per cent. At the same time, the main rate of VAT has risen from 8 per cent to 17.5 per cent and the base of the tax has been widened.

The following is just a selection of measures which would begin to reverse this increase in economic inequality. Most would provide funds for some of the health-promoting measures contained in this chapter and elsewhere in this book.

- *Abolish the upper earnings limit for employee national insurance contributions (NIC)*: employees currently pay no contributions on gross earnings above a given limit (£430 per week from April 1994); removing this anomaly could raise more than £3 billion and would substantially reduce inequalities in post-tax incomes.

- *Restrict the value of the main personal tax allowance to 20 per cent for all taxpayers:* under the present system the existence of a tax-free allowance is of more value to a higher-rate taxpayer than to a standard or lower-rate taxpayer. This is because a higher rate taxpayer saves 40 per cent of the value of the allowance, whereas a standard-rate taxpayer saves only 25 per cent of the value of the allowance and a lower-rate taxpayer 20 per cent. If the allowance had the same effective value to all taxpayers (as is now the case with the married couple's allowance), this would raise £5–6 billion and would take most money from the highest earners.

- *Increase the highest rate of income tax:* although it would probably be counter-productive to return to the punitive marginal tax rates of the late 1970s, many European countries have top tax rates of around 50 per cent compared with the UK's 40 per cent. Each 1 per cent on the top tax rate raises around £330 million.

- *Increase reliance on income tax and reduce taxes on spending:* without increasing overall taxation it would be possible to reduce income inequality simply by relying more on income taxes (including NICs) and less on VAT, which bears more heavily on poorer households. In principle this argument would also imply lower duties on alcohol and tobacco but this conflicts with other health objectives (see Chapter 6).

It should be stressed that none of these revenue-raising measures represents a 'free lunch'. The only way to raise large sums of this sort is by taking money from large numbers of people. It is therefore important that in pressing for such measures there should also be nurtured a political consensus for the purposes for which the money is to be spent.

Conclusions

The links between family poverty and poor health are strong and clear, and it is families with children who are particularly likely to be among the poorest households. The main groups affected are the children of people who are unemployed, of lone parents and of people with low wages. Policies that enable parents to re-enter the labour market and improve the social security system for those left dependent on benefits offer the best prospects for relieving family poverty and improving the health of parents and children alike. However, if the policy goal is a reduction in economic inequalities *per se*, then very radical changes to the tax benefit system would have to be considered.

CHAPTER **6**

The burden of smoking

Joy Townsend

Introduction

Cigarettes are acknowledged to be the greatest single cause of premature mortality and morbidity in the UK, accounting for 18 per cent of all deaths (111,000) and over one-third of those in middle age (HEA, 1991). Britain still has among the highest smoking-related death rates in the world from lung cancer, coronary heart disease and chronic obstructive airways disease (WHO, 1988). The damage from these conditions is largely irreversible by the time they are diagnosed, and life expectancy is short.

The numbers of people who smoke have been reduced substantially, but in such a way that it has become, relatively speaking, a habit of people in disadvantaged circumstances. Most of the fall in cigarette consumption over the last three decades has occurred in higher income groups. However, it is by no means inevitable that the decline will continue unless there are clear policies to counteract the effects of advertising, price erosion and rising incomes. In fact, in the late 1980s, when cigarette prices fell relative to inflation, regular smoking by 15-year-old girls rose from 20 per cent to 25 per cent (Lader and Matheson, 1991) and by 16–19-year-old girls from 28 per cent to 32 per cent (OPCS, 1991b).

The purpose of this chapter is to assess what policies could be adopted to reduce smoking levels, particularly among people in disadvantaged circumstances, and hence narrow inequalities in health. First, however, the chapter begins by examining the social distribution of smoking and how it has changed over the last few decades. It also considers the high costs of smoking borne by people with poor socioeconomic circumstances. Evidence about the link between smoking and health is then briefly reviewed, and in particular how smoking contributes to inequalities in health. Finally, the chapter sets out the different strategies available to reduce smoking and the recommendations that emerged from the discussion at Ditchley Park.

Who smokes?

In the last twenty years evidence from the *General Household Survey* (GHS) shows that the prevalence of smoking in all age groups has fallen by about 40 per cent (Thomas *et al.*, 1994). For young people aged 16–19 and 20–24 this reduction occurred mostly in the

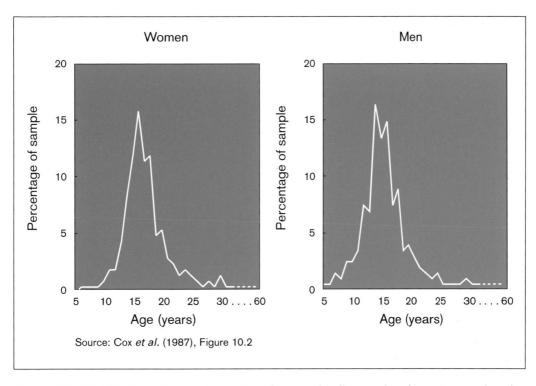

Source: Cox *et al.* (1987), Figure 10.2

Figure 6.1: Distribution of age when started to smoke (in regular cigarette smokers), *Health and Lifestyle Survey,* **Great Britain, 1985–86**

1970s, and prevalence settled around 30 per cent and 38 per cent respectively. For older smokers the reduction occurred later, mostly within the last ten years. The highest prevalence of smoking is in the 20–34-year age range (about 35 per cent), with little difference in rates between men and women. About 20 per cent of people over 60 smoke.

In designing prevention policies it is important to be aware of when and why people begin smoking. As can be seen from Figure 6.1, the peak ages for taking up smoking for both men and women are around 14–16 years old, and after the age of 20 very few people take up regular smoking (Cox *et al.*, 1987).

Before the 1960s, when the adverse health effects of cigarette smoking were first widely reported (RCP, 1962), there was little difference between the smoking habits of different social groups. As can be seen from Figure 6.2, in 1958 around 60 per cent of men and 42 per cent of women in each socioeconomic group smoked cigarettes. Since then there has been a divergence in smoking by social group and a narrowing of the difference between men and women. In 1992, as Figure 6.2 shows, only 14 per cent of professional men and 13 per cent of professional women smoked, against 35 per cent of women and 42 per cent of men in unskilled manual occupations. Men and women smokers in disadvantaged socioeconomic groups are also far less likely to smoke low-tar cigarettes: 11 per cent of men and 18 per cent of women smokers in unskilled occupations compared with 29 per cent of men and 51 per cent of women smokers in professional groups (Thomas *et al.*, 1994).

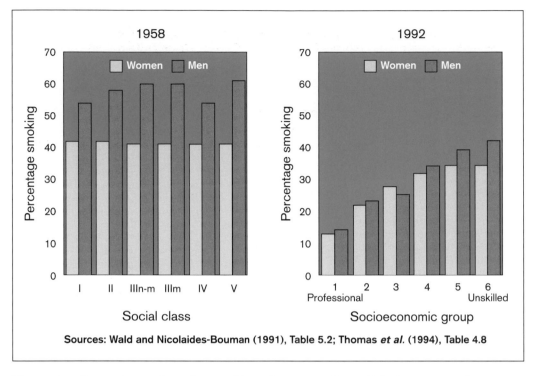

Figure 6.2: Percentage of adults smoking cigarettes, Great Britain, 1958 and 1992

A number of recent reports have identified much higher current cigarette smoking prevalence among some of the most disadvantaged groups in the UK. The 1992 GHS shows that just under half (46 per cent) of people who are unemployed smoked, compared with 29 per cent of those working and 36 per cent of those economically inactive. Smoking levels are highest among the widowed, divorced or separated (Thomas *et al.*, 1994).

High smoking rates are also reported for young married people under 24 years old, particularly those with dependent children, for whom the smoking prevalence of men is 54 per cent and of women 43 per cent (Smyth and Browne, 1992). There has also been evidence for some time now that lone mothers have uncommonly high smoking rates (Marsh and Matheson, 1983). Recently, Marsh and MacKay (1994) reported that smoking prevalence increased with markers of increasing disadvantage. Nearly 70 per cent of lone parents with low incomes, no educational qualifications, living in council housing and from manual occupations were regular smokers. For those who had any one of these disadvantages, about half smoked; for those with two or three disadvantages, two-thirds smoked. However, Afro-Caribbean and Asian families did not show these higher smoking rates.

Expenditure

Marsh and Mackay (1994) report that one-half of lone parents and three-quarters of couples on income support typically spent a fifth of the adult component of their income support on cigarettes. In effect, a considerable proportion of social security benefits given to families with low incomes is being 'clawed back' by the Treasury in cigarette taxes.

Table 6.1: Percentage of household income spent on cigarettes by household type and income group, *Family Expenditure Survey,* Great Britain, 1961–92

Household type	Income group	Year				
		1961	1975	1980	1990	1992
Man and woman + child	Lowest quartile	6.8	4.8	4.8	3.5	4.3
	2nd quartile	6.1	4.3	3.4	1.8	2.1
	3rd quartile	6.0	3.4	3.0	1.7	1.7
	Highest quartile	5.8	2.4	1.4	0.7	0.8
Man and woman + 2 children	Lowest quartile	6.4	3.9	4.7	3.5	4.1
	2nd quartile	6.0	3.4	3.1	2.2	2.6
	3rd quartile	5.7	2.6	2.6	1.6	1.4
	Highest quartile	4.4	2.1	1.4	0.6	0.6

Sources: DE (1962; 1976; 1981); CSO (1991; 1993)

Table 6.1 shows the percentage of household income spent on cigarettes by couples with one or two children for each income quartile of the population for a selection of years between 1961 and 1992. Although the average proportion of income spent on cigarettes has fallen for all groups since 1961, compared with higher income groups those in the poorest quartile of the population currently spend a relatively higher proportion of their (much lower) income on cigarettes. For example, in 1992 a couple with one child in the

Table 6.2: Weekly expenditure on tobacco by families with two adults and two children (at 1993 prices), *Family Expenditure Survey,* Great Britain, 1980–92

Income group	1980 (£)	1986 (£)	1990 (£)	1992 (£)
Lowest quartile	9.36	9.47	9.72	9.57
2nd quartile	7.64	7.84	8.05	7.99
3rd quartile	7.74	7.10	6.32	5.56
Highest quartile	6.23	4.29	3.80	3.80

Sources: DE (1981; 1987); CSO (1991; 1993)

lowest income quartile spent more than five times the proportion of their incomes on cigarettes as those in the highest income quartile; thirty years earlier the differential was less than 20 per cent.

Table 6.2 shows changes in the actual levels of spending on tobacco at constant prices by families consisting of two adults and two children, by household income groups. Between 1980 and 1992 tobacco-related expenditure remained broadly constant for families in the poorest half of the income distribution. In contrast, levels of expenditure on tobacco fell substantially for those in the top half.

Summary

Smoking prevalence is highest among people with poor socioeconomic circumstances. The decline in smoking rates over the last few decades has been much lower among such people than others. The evidence suggests that smoking rates may be particularly high among people who are unemployed and young adults with families, especially lone parents. Not only do people in families with low incomes have high smoking rates, but they spend a disproportionately large share of their income on cigarettes. Smoking therefore not only directly harms their health but also decreases the resources available to them more generally.

Smoking and inequalities in health

Compared to non-smokers, smokers are at high or very high risk of dying from many diseases: about a twentyfold higher risk from lung cancer, a tenfold risk from chronic obstructive airways disease and a 1.5 to threefold risk from coronary heart disease (Peto *et al.*, 1992). On the other hand, the relative risks fall significantly when smokers give up. For example, at any given age, a person who has smoked for thirty-five years has three times the risk of dying from lung cancer as someone who smoked for twenty-five years and gave up for ten.

Smoking also increases the risks of stroke, atherosclerotic aortic aneurysm, peripheral vascular disease and cancer of the larynx, mouth, oesophagus, bladder, liver, pancreas, kidney, stomach and cervix (US Department of Health and Human Services, 1989). Furthermore, smoking increases the risks associated with pregnancy, perinatal mortality and low birthweight. Children in families where some members smoke are at greater risk of respiratory problems and leukaemia.

In relation to inequalities in health, the high concentration of smoking among more disadvantaged social groups in preceding decades is reflected in the distribution of smoking-related deaths in the early 1980s (OPCS, 1986b). As Table 6.3 shows, a man in an unskilled manual occupation is more than four times as likely to die of lung cancer as a professional and twice as likely to die from coronary heart disease. For women there is a threefold difference for lung cancer and a fourfold difference for heart disease. For some diseases these patterns are new. There was no difference in lung cancer mortality by different social groups before 1961, and the social gradient for coronary heart disease has reversed: mortality used to be higher in professional and managerial groups. For lung cancer, heart disease and chronic bronchitis, the inequalities between manual and non-manual groups widened between 1971 and 1981.

Table 6.3: Standardised mortality ratios from smoking diseases by social class, England and Wales, 1979–80, 1982–83, adults aged 15–64

Social class	Lung cancer		Coronary heart disease		Chronic obstructive airways disease	
	Men	Women	Men	Women	Men	Women
Professional	43	48	70	43	34	34
Skilled manual	120	115	109	113	110	102
Unskilled manual	178	149	144	161	211	170

Source: OPCS (1986b)

It is almost certain that differences in smoking levels and smoking cessation are important causal factors in the observed mortality differentials between social classes for the diseases illustrated in Table 6.3. Moreover, there is no room for doubt that smoking-related diseases make a major contribution to perpetuating health inequalities. This does not by any means imply that the health divide has a single cause. Studies that have adjusted for variations in smoking between social groups still report substantial differentials in mortality (Marmot et al., 1984).

Policy options

There are a number of ways in which smoking can be reduced:

- by reducing recruitment to smoking, particularly in the peak years of adolescence;
- by current smokers giving up;
- by current smokers cutting down.

In addition, death from smoking diseases effectively reduces the number of smokers by 110,000 annually.

Logically, the most obvious focus of policy intervention would be reducing recruitment among teenagers, when smoking starts. Much of the high smoking rates of lone parents on low incomes are also at young ages. Unfortunately, policies aimed at adolescents have not had notable success, possibly because uptake is most highly related to parental and peer-group behaviour and attitudes to smoking. Another factor may be that programmes have not sufficiently addressed the fact that teenagers do smoke and may be in need of cessation support.

There is, however, a considerable body of international knowledge on strategies to reduce adult smoking, and experts in the UK have played an important role in their development.

Less is known about the impact of policies on smokers from different social groups, although there is evidence related to some policies.

There are six main policy options available to discourage smoking. Two focus on enabling individuals to increase their knowledge, skills or coping mechanisms in dealing with smoking reduction. These are programmes of health education and smoking cessation advice or support. Three further strategies are based on legislative measures aiming to change the environment by reducing exposure to tobacco promotion and cigarette smoke: controlling tobacco advertising and sponsorship; restricting availability; and creating smoke-free public places. The final option is the fiscal one of increasing taxes on cigarettes to discourage consumption. Each of these potential interventions will be considered in turn.

Health education

The effects of the Royal College of Physicians reports (RCP, 1962; 1971), which publicised the relationship between smoking and health, together with the television ban on cigarette advertising, are estimated to have reduced smoking by 5 per cent in 1962, 1965 and 1971 (Atkinson and Skegg, 1973). Subsequent and sustained anti-smoking information over the last two decades has played a major part in reducing smoking in the UK. Hamilton (1972) reports for the USA that health education had a significant effect over the period 1953–70 and reduced cigarette consumption by 14 per cent per year. Mass media campaigns against smoking are not always successful, but the potential effectiveness of sensitive campaigns is clear, both on a national and on a local basis. For example, in Australia reductions of 6–11 per cent have been reported from New South Wales mass media campaigns (Egger et al., 1983).

School health education has resulted in a high level of awareness of the risks of smoking and has influenced pupils' attitudes (Catford et al., 1984). However, studies have failed to show that the provision of information affects teenagers' decisions to start smoking (Murray et al., 1984; Cleary et al., 1986), although there is some evidence that it may delay uptake.

Health education is countered by tobacco company advertising, and there is evidence that this is an important factor in promoting and reinforcing smoking among young people, as discussed below. However, it has been suggested that substantial and sustained health education might reduce smoking by 10 per cent by the end of the century (Atkinson and Townsend, 1977). Unfortunately, over the last thirty years health education seems to have influenced advantaged social groups more than disadvantaged and men more than women, although this has been less true in recent years. Clearly this imbalance needs to be addressed directly if smoking levels are to be reduced among people in disadvantaged circumstances.

The effectiveness of different educational approaches has been reviewed by Whitehead (1989). This suggests that although some success has been achieved with programmes for some sections of the population, they are unlikely to be effective with disadvantaged social and economic groups unless sensitive to the circumstances in which such people live, and backed up by wider policies to create a supportive environment. More importantly, the need to develop different and sensitive approaches to the issue of smoking reduction with women on low income has been advocated by ASH (1992) and Blackburn and Graham (1992).

Smoking cessation advice and support

Verbal and written advice given during a normal general practice consultation has been shown to be highly effective (Jamrozik *et al.*, 1984) and cost-effective (Williams, 1985) in persuading people to give up smoking, especially if there is follow-up. These studies suggest that such advice might reduce smoking prevalence by as much as 5 per cent (Jamrozik *et al.*, 1984). A study of adolescents invited for a general practice health check (Townsend *et al.*, 1991) has shown that 60 per cent of 13–17-year-olds who smoked were willing to make an agreement with their GP or practice nurse to give up. This may be an effective way of reducing teenage smoking, and further studies are needed to evaluate long-term effects.

Providing advice about cessation may be most effective when carried out during the course of a consultation for a health problem, as smokers, particularly those from disadvantaged social and economic groups, have been shown to be reluctant to attend special health promotion clinics (Sanders *et al.*, 1989). This approach may be encouraged by the economic incentives now being introduced for GPs for recording patients' cigarette consumption. As people in disadvantaged circumstances both consult their GPs more frequently and smoke more, opportunistic general practice support is likely to have most effect for them.

A number of different approaches have been suggested. For example, one controlled trial of three different educational strategies used in GP consultations found that a practical demonstration of the effects of smoking on the lungs was more effective in discouraging smoking in groups with less formal education (Jamrozik *et al.*, 1984). Evidence also suggests that, in relation to smokers in disadvantaged circumstances, health-care workers must take account of the broader experiences of their lives. For example, the Newcastle community midwifery care project provided enhanced midwifery care at home as well as increased access to other services. Twice as many mothers in the project gave up smoking or reduced their consumption of cigarettes as in the control group (Graham, 1993b).

It is important to consider smoking cessation in this wider context, as severe stress is cited by many smokers as a barrier to giving up and the relief obtained from psychological pressure is given as a reason for continuing to use cigarettes. The high smoking rates of those who are unemployed, divorced and separated and lone parents appear to confirm this. The overwhelming and immediate problems of poverty, isolation and powerlessness may well militate against considerations of health. There is evidence, however, of a certain circularity between stress and smoking. Alternative explanations of this differ in the emphasis placed on the positive effect of smoking and the negative effects of tobacco deprivation (Parrott, 1994). The nicotine resource model emphasises that smoking modifies mood, reducing the smoker's feelings of anxiety and anger (Warburton, 1992). The deprivation reversal model holds that the smoker gets nothing from smoking, but smokes only to prevent withdrawal (Schachter, 1978). Two recent longitudinal studies tend to confirm the latter model: smoking cessation reduces stress and resumption increases stress (Cohen and Lichtenstein, 1990; Parrott *et al.*, 1993).

This finding has considerable implications for policy. It is consistent with a model in which young people start smoking, mostly under age, and continue to smoke partly or largely to counter the stress of withdrawal. If this is so, it may be worth putting a lot of effort into cessation programmes with potential benefits, particularly to those with low incomes, of more money, better health and less stress. In this respect it may be beneficial to consider making nicotine replacement therapy available on NHS prescription, at least to those on income support or family credit or those who are unemployed.

Controlling advertising and tobacco sponsorship

Each year the tobacco industry spends about £100 million on advertising and promoting tobacco products in the UK (ASH, 1993). There has been much dispute about the influence of advertising on the number of cigarettes smoked. The tobacco industry argues that its advertising does not recruit smokers or increase consumption, but only influences choice of brand (Tobacco Advisory Council, 1992). The effects of an influence as complex as advertising are not easy to model, but analysis suggests that in the 1970s a 10 per cent increase in advertising expenditure in the UK increased smoking by 1 per cent (Johnson, 1975). Similar effects have been shown for New Zealand (Chetwynd et al., 1988) and the reinforcing effects of cigarette advertising on 11–14-year-old children in Glasgow have been demonstrated by Aitken and Eadie (1990).

What the effects of a total advertising ban would be are not entirely clear, but estimates from a number of studies suggest a fall in cigarette consumption of about 10 per cent (Laugesen and Meades, 1990). For example, 'before' and 'after' estimates for New Zealand (with no concurrent price changes) suggest there was about a 7.5 per cent fall following their ban on cigarette advertising (Harrison and Chetwynd, 1990). The Department of Health's report on the subject concluded that tobacco advertising bans in different countries have had sizeable and significant effects on smoking (DoH, 1992). If the proposed European Community directive to ban tobacco advertising across the Community were adopted, a reasonable average estimate is that it might reduce smoking by the order of 7.5 per cent (Townsend, 1993).

There is little direct evidence of the effects of advertising on different social groups. Cigarette advertising is now, however, more predominant in poorer areas (Matthews, 1986) and forms a higher proportion of advertising in the tabloid press than in broadsheet papers. Children are very aware of cigarette advertisements, like them and can interpret at least some of their messages (Aitken et al., 1985). Cigarette advertising has also been found to encourage smoking in teenagers by reinforcing the adolescent's image of him or herself as successful, witty, exciting and glamorous (Ledwith, 1984). An advertising ban might well have most effect on people with low incomes and on recruitment to smoking at young ages.

Restricting availability

Cigarettes and tobacco are among the most readily available of all products in terms of number of outlets and hours of availability. Although not legally available to those under 16, under-age sales are still widespread and are the main source for under-age teenage smoking. Restricting availability is therefore a strategy that might contribute to discouraging the onset of smoking at the peak age for recruitment. This might be done by increasing the legal age for buying cigarettes to 18, in line with the minimum age for buying alcohol. This already holds in some other countries and would have the advantage of making it easier to identify under-age smokers. If smoking uptake could be delayed to 18 this would almost certainly reduce the rate of regular smoking in adults, although it is not possible to judge to what degree this might be.

Creating smoke-free environments

Non-smokers who experience lifetime exposure to environmental smoke have an increased risk of lung cancer of 10–30 per cent (US Surgeon General, 1986). The Froggat Report (Independent Scientific Committee on Smoking and Health, 1988) identified many deleterious effects of passive smoking on respiratory function, signs and symptoms and childhood development. In addition, it found that adults with asthma may experience substantial decline in lung function from an hour's exposure to sidestream smoke (passive smoking). These findings have added to the arguments for creating smoke-free environments, particularly in public places and where people work. In addition, recognition of the public fire hazards of smoking have accelerated the provision of smoke-free transport.

There is still a long way to go, however, to catch up with the best practices of countries such as Canada, the USA and several states in Australia. A European Community resolution has been adopted restricting smoking in enclosed places open to the public, including public transport. Implementation within the UK would support *The Health of the Nation* smoking targets (Cm 1986, 1992), and recent guidelines from the Department of the Environment urge that progress in this direction should be more rapid. It has been recommended by the Faculty of Public Health Medicine (1991) that all schools and hospitals should provide a smoke-free environment. Disadvantaged social and economic groups have a higher smoking prevalence, make more use of public transport and are more likely to be working with smokers, and so are most likely to benefit from such policies.

Pricing policy

Cigarette taxation is another arm of policy with particular potential for affecting the level of smoking. Taxation makes up the major part of the price of cigarettes, but its relative importance has sometimes been eroded with inflation. The five distinct trend periods in UK cigarette consumption over the last twenty years have each been mirrored by a trend in the real price of cigarettes in the opposite direction. As can be seen in Figure 6.3, smoking not only decreased when prices rose, but also clearly rose when the price of cigarettes did not keep up with inflation. Similar increases or decreases in smoking with price fluctuations have been shown for France (Insée Comptes Nationaux, 1990), Canada (Sweanor, 1991) and New Zealand (Sweanor, 1992).

To quantify the response to changes in price or income, economists calculate a price elasticity. This can be defined as the percentage change in the quantity of cigarettes bought, for a 1 per cent change in the price. The responsiveness of cigarette consumption to changes in real price, has been measured using a variety of models, giving estimates of the price elasticity of demand for cigarettes from -0.4 to -0.86, clustering around -0.55 (Godfrey and Maynard, 1988; Pekurinen, 1991). This means, for instance, that a 1 per cent rise in relative cigarette price results in about 0.55 per cent fall in the amount smoked.

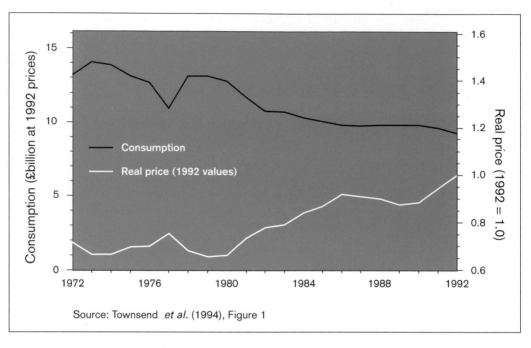

Source: Townsend *et al.* (1994), Figure 1

Figure 6.3: The relationship between consumption and the real price of cigarettes, Great Britain, 1972–92

Conversely, a 1 per cent fall in price results in a 0.55 per cent rise in the amount smoked. Estimates have been surprisingly robust over time and place (Stone, 1945; Lewit and Coate, 1982; Worgotter and Kunze, 1986; Townsend, 1988; Scott, 1991; Townsend *et al.*, 1994).

Most of the economic studies analyse the number of cigarettes smoked per adult or per household, as this is easier to model and estimate than actual smoking prevalence. However, for the USA, Lewit and Coate (1982) have estimated the 'smoking prevalence' price elasticity as -0.3, whereas the quantity smoked per adult effect was -0.1. That is, a 1 per cent rise in price results in about a 0.3 per cent reduction in smoking prevalence and a 0.1 per cent reduction in the quantity smoked per adult. This suggests that price has more influence on whether people smoke or not than on how much they smoke.

Price elasticity is particularly high among people in disadvantaged circumstances and teenagers. For example, an elasticity of -1.0 in the UK has been estimated for unskilled manual workers (Townsend, *et al.*, 1994) and -1.4 for teenagers in the USA (Lewit *et al.*, 1981). Recent rapid price rises in Canada have been associated with halving of smoking prevalence in 15–19-year-olds from 45 per cent to 22 per cent between 1980 and 1988 (Sweanor, 1991). This evidence suggests that, on average, people with poor socioeconomic circumstances, and possibly teenagers, not only reduce levels of consumption but also total expenditure on cigarettes when there is a price rise.

The clear implication of these analyses is that substantial increases in cigarette prices would narrow the health divide. Raising relative prices could be expected to narrow the differentials in smoking prevalence and consumption between social and economic groups. Unfortunately, a direct consequence of such policies would be to further reduce the real incomes of people in poverty who continue to smoke.

One question debated at great length at Ditchley Park, therefore, was whether the price of cigarettes should be held down to avoid hardship to families with poor economic circumstances. The difficulty with this is that price mostly affects smoking by lower income groups, and has most impact where health education has least. Indeed, it has been argued that the fall in the real price of cigarettes of 40 per cent between 1965 and 1980 in the UK largely countered the effects of health education to people in disadvantaged circumstances and was a major factor in the divergence of smoking prevalence by social and economic groups (J. Townsend, 1987). Price has also fallen relative to average incomes. Erosion of cigarette prices could be detrimental to public health, particularly to the health of lower income groups. The dynamic relationship between smoking, health and inequalities stretches over a lifetime and price is a potential force to break this link at any stage, reducing the harmful effects in terms of smokers' health and that of their children.

On balance the prevailing view was that price increases have an important role to play in discouraging tobacco consumption, but that the poorest groups of persistent smokers need considerable additional assistance to help them stop. In fact, it seems increasingly likely that the most effective way of aiding this would be to substantially improve the overall socioeconomic circumstances of those who are most disadvantaged. Although this is an important message for the book as a whole, it goes beyond the specific remit of this chapter.

Priorities

The Ditchley Park seminar concluded that smoking seriously exacerbates inequalities in health. It was acknowledged that there is a need to continue to invest in general health education about smoking risks and to provide cessation support for smokers as set out in *Smoke Free for Health*, the Department of Health's recent document (DoH, 1994a). In addition, four major changes in policy were advocated to support smoking reduction aimed at reducing inequalities in health by concentrating on people with poor socioeconomic circumstances.

The first priority is to ban the advertising and promotion of cigarettes and other tobacco products in the UK, in line with the European Community proposal. The costs of this would not be sizeable in national terms and would be borne mainly by the tobacco industry in terms of reduced sales, an inevitable consequence of any tobacco reduction policy, and the industry would of course be saved the costs of advertising. There might be a financial loss to the advertising industry and press, but experience from other countries suggests that this has been minimal (ASH, 1993). The government would experience a loss of revenue proportional to the effect of the ban on consumption, possibly of 7 per cent (£550 million), which could be recouped by increased taxes, as detailed below.

Secondly, it is proposed that new resources should be invested in improved development and evaluation of innovative health education interventions targeted at high-risk groups of smokers. Evidence suggests that such measures need to be broad and to take account of the constraints and pressures of people's lives.

Thirdly, additional resources should be found for the development and evaluation of specific cessation support programmes to those considered to be the most vulnerable groups of smokers – those on low incomes, those who are unemployed and adolescents. These interventions might include advice by primary care workers during consultations, nicotine patches on prescription or assisting people in disadvantaged circumstances to cope with caring responsibilities and financial problems which may enable them to reduce their reliance on cigarettes.

Finally, after much debate about pricing policy, it was argued that cigarette taxes should be increased as part of a positive step to reduce smoking across the population. However, this should not be done without concurrent attempts to ameliorate the financial and social hardship and isolation experienced by those on very low incomes, particularly women bringing up children on their own.

CHAPTER **7**

The role of the NHS

Michaela Benzeval, Ken Judge and Margaret Whitehead

Introduction

There is little evidence that variations in the quantity and quality of health services between advanced industrialised countries make a substantial difference to crude measures of health status such as national mortality rates. For example, in a recent study of OECD countries, Babazono and Hillman (1994) concluded that 'total health care spending per capita and out-patient and in-patient utilisation are not related to health outcomes' (p. 376). As Fox and Benzeval have shown in Chapter 2, health inequalities are primarily the product of differences in living standards. Levels of wellbeing and life expectancy are more closely related to the availability of decent social security, housing, employment and education than health care. Nevertheless, whatever the relative importance of health services in comparison with other areas of social policy:

> *any inequality in the availability and use of health services in relation to need is in itself socially unjust and requires alleviation.*
>
> (Townsend and Davidson, 1982, p. 68)

It would be quite wrong, therefore, to assume that the Department of Health and the NHS have no role to play in promoting and developing purposive policies that promote social justice and tackle inequalities in health. In fact they have three key obligations:

- to ensure that resources are distributed between local areas in proportion to their relative needs;

- to respond appropriately to the health care needs of different social groups;

- to take the lead in encouraging a wider and more strategic approach to developing healthy public policies.

The purpose of this chapter is to consider these requirements. First, it considers resource allocation mechanisms within the NHS. What evidence is there that resources are distributed according to need and how might the process be improved? Secondly, it considers the delivery of health care services. Is there equitable access to health care for individuals from different social groups? What interventions are available that enable individuals in disadvantaged circumstances to have improved access to services that can both alleviate sickness and promote health? Thirdly, the chapter considers the wider role that the Department of Health and local health purchasers must adopt. At a national level, what mechanisms exist within Whitehall to ensure that all departments take account of the impact of their policies on inequalities in health? At a local level, how can purchasers work with other agencies to directly influence the wide range of economic, social and environmental factors that determine people's health?

It should be noted here that the contents of this chapter were not discussed in detail at the Ditchley Park Seminar. However, we have tried to follow both the logic and spirit of the discussions that took place there.

Resource allocation

The real nature and extent of inequality in access to health care in Britain is difficult to establish, but there are certainly no grounds for complacency. Health care needs vary between social groups, and the geographical distribution of such groups also varies. At the very least, therefore, it will continue to be important to ensure that health care resources are distributed in proportion to the relative needs of local health authorities.

When the NHS was created there were substantial variations in the health care resources available to different parts of the country reflecting 'past philanthropy, municipal pride and local affluence rather than a planned response to population needs' (Beech *et al.*, 1990, p. 44). Some of the most serious inequalities were dealt with by the Medical Practices Committee (MPC), which helped to establish a fairer distribution of family doctors quite quickly after 1948 (Butler *et al.*, 1973). Similarly, bringing hospitals and their staff into the public sector improved access for many people. However, little was done to tackle the maldistribution of resources for hospital services in any systematic way until the 1970s.

The aim of this section is to describe how the NHS in England distributes its resources with respect to its two main funding streams: hospital and community health services (HCHS) and family health services (FHS).

Hospital and community health services

The most significant block of NHS expenditure – 60 per cent – is made available to regional health authorities for HCHS through a system of resource allocation that has evolved since 1976. The then Labour government established a Resource Allocation Working Party (RAWP) charged with reviewing:

> the arrangements for distributing NHS capital and revenue to RHAs, AHAs and districts respectively with a view to establishing a method of securing, as soon as practicable, a pattern of distribution responsive objectively, equitably and efficiently to relative need and to make recommendations.

> (DHSS, 1976, p. 5)

RAWP recommended that financial allocation for regional health authorities should be based on population estimates that had been adjusted to take account of local variations in:

- national age- and gender-specific hospital utilisation rates;
- standardised mortality ratios;
- the excess costs of service provision in London and the south east;
- inter-regional flows of patients.

This weighted population approach was used to produce financial targets for regions which could be compared with prevailing allocations so as to enable ministers to judge the degree to which redistribution could take place. By the mid-1980s the RAWP formula had achieved considerable success in the sense that nearly all regions had moved much closer to their target allocations, but the process of redistribution at a time of tight financial constraints engendered considerable tension and criticisms. In 1986 therefore the Management Board of the NHS decided to reconsider how best to allocate resources for hospital and community services.

The Review of RAWP (DHSS, 1988) took a radically different approach to its predecessor by basing its analysis on the assumption that careful analysis of small area differences in hospital utilisation would yield useful estimates of relative need for health care. The key result was the identification of a quantitative relationship between SMRs and the use of hospital beds (Royston *et al.*, 1992), which was incorporated – albeit in a modified form – into the weighted capitation system introduced by the *Working for Patients* reforms in 1991 (Cm 555, 1989).

The weighted capitation approach involved adjusting the population size of RHAs to take account of differences in age structure, health care needs – measured by SMRs – and the cost of delivering services (Judge and Mays, 1994a). However, the assumptions and methods involved in weighted capitation were seriously criticised for a number of reasons.

- The needs factor – based on the relationship between utilisation and SMRs – failed to take sufficient account of the socioeconomic determinants of the demand for health care (Sheldon, Davey Smith and Bevan, 1993), and was derived on the basis of inappropriate methods (Mays, 1989; Carr-Hill and Sheldon, 1992; Sheldon and Carr-Hill, 1992).

- The age-cost adjustment over-compensated for the costs of providing health care to older people. In part this was because it excluded the costs of day cases and did not distinguish between differences in treatment costs that are known to vary with age (Smith *et al.*, 1994).

- The population projections were subject to considerable uncertainty, especially for some sub-groups that are intensive users of health care such as over 85s (Raftery, 1993).

- The extra finance for London and the south east was determined without a secure empirical grounding (Judge and Mays, 1994a).

Some of these weaknesses were clearly recognised when, in February 1993, ministers announced a review of the existing system of weighted capitation, although the primary rationale given was that:

the availability of the 1991 census data presented a need and an opportunity to review the formula because it provides up-to-date information on population and social characteristics. It also included, for the first time, a direct question on morbidity.

(NHSE, 1994a, p. 2)

As a result of the review, the allocation of HCHS resources will continue to be informed by a process of adjusting population estimates to take account of differences in the age structure, needs and relative costs of service provision between areas (NHSE, 1994a). However, each of the three sets of adjustments have been refined in different ways. First, the estimated average costs of providing hospital care to different age groups has been revised so that slightly less weight is given to older populations. Secondly, a much more sophisticated statistical analysis of the small area factors associated with the costs of hospital utilisation, undertaken by a research team at the University of York, has informed the choice of a new need index. Finally, the Economic and Operational Research Division of the Department of Health has developed a new market forces factor that 'recognises four pay zones for staff costs and reflects geographical differences in land values and building costs' (FDL(94)68, para. 9).

Of these three changes, it is the work done by the York team in developing a new need index that could make the largest contribution to ensuring that areas of high deprivation are properly compensated for their health care needs. For example, the researchers themselves suggest that the application of their results 'would redistribute funds towards inner city areas' (Smith *et al.*, 1994, p. 1053) that tend to be the most deprived and to have the highest health care needs. Insofar as this is true then the review of weighted capitation represents a welcome move in the direction of ensuring equity of access to health care in England. Unfortunately, some serious question marks remain both about the analysis of needs conducted by the York team and the way in which their results have been used by the Department of Health.

In a review of the York work, Judge and Mays (1994b) conclude that it makes use of 'much more comprehensive data and more sophisticated statistical methods that are better informed by theory than hitherto' (p. 1031). It also represents 'a major advance in assessing the relative health care needs of small areas. ... Nevertheless, some problems remain that are mainly due to inadequacies in the data available for analysis' (p. 1032). What is more worrying than any methodological or data weaknesses in the York work, however, is the way in which the results have been used by the Department of Health. The potential redistributive impact of the new need index has been significantly reduced by the government's decision not to attach any need weight at all to almost one-quarter of all hospital in-patient utilisation. This is a particularly disturbing development because it implies that the long-standing commitment 'to ensure an equitable distribution of resources' is being watered down by the emphasis on 'safeguarding continuity and stability in the NHS' (FDL(94)68, para. 2).

Unfortunately, it is difficult to evaluate the impact of the changes in any precise way because 'a number of policy and organisation changes which will affect resource allocation' (FDL(94)68, para. 1) are in the pipeline and how these will all turn out remains uncertain. For example, the abolition of regional health authorities in 1996 will mean a single national formula will be used to determine weighted capitation shares for district health authorities.

In addition, it remains unclear how resources for GP fundholders will be allocated (Sheldon *et al.*, 1994), even though there is evidence that some of them have received more than their fair share (Dixon *et al.*, 1994).

More generally, the principle of allocating resources to HCHS in isolation from any consideration of the distribution of primary and social care is a serious mistake (Judge and Mays, 1994b). Hospital, primary, community and social services act as both complements and substitutes for each other. For example, the availability of social care services, such as day centres, home helps and residential homes, can have an important impact on the ability of health authorities to meet the needs of their populations. There are wide variations in the availability and use of residential care that are not obviously related to need or NHS resource allocation (Judge and Mays, 1994a). Data from the 1991 census indicate that there is a twofold difference between shire counties in the proportion of the population aged 75 and over living in non-NHS residential and nursing homes. The range was even greater for metropolitan areas, from 2.2 per cent in the City of Westminster to 17 per cent in Sefton (OPCS, 1991a). Failure to take account of the availability of other services in the distribution of HCHS monies, therefore, is likely to exacerbate inequalities in access to care.

Family health services

The second largest element of NHS spending – 22 per cent – is made available for FHS, which includes GPs and related services, drugs, dentists and opticians. Although direct expenditure on GPs only accounts for just over one-quarter of total FHS spending, they are the critical players in determining the quality of consultations, access to drugs and support services and in acting as gatekeepers to the hospital sector. A key requirement for promoting equity of access to health care, therefore, is to ensure that the geographical distribution and quality of GPs and the support available to them is in proportion to the needs for them.

The distribution of GPs is controlled by the MPC, which tries, through a process of negative direction, to equalise the list size of GPs between areas. Nevertheless, there are substantial variations at the local level. For example, in 1993 there were 8.4 whole-time equivalent GPs per 10,000 patients in Manchester compared with only 5.6 in Rotherham (DoH, 1993). In fact, these statistics understate the real extent of inequality because they fail to take account of variations in the underlying needs of different populations, such as differences in the age structure or the prevalence of morbidity, which can influence the demand for health care.

In addition, a number of studies have shown that the structure of GP services is often inadequate in areas of high deprivation, particularly in inner London. Poor provision of GP services in these areas includes factors such as the lack of availability of GPs out of hours, the higher proportion of GPs who are single-handed or over 65, and the poor quality of premises (Boyle and Smaje, 1993). Baker (1992) has shown how factors such as these, together with the level of deprivation in a practice area, are closely associated with the standard and development of primary care services. Thus not only is the distribution of GPs unrelated to need but there also appears to be an inverse relationship between the quality of care and disadvantaged areas.

The most important policy response to evidence about poor access to primary care in areas of high need was the introduction in 1990 of deprivation payments. GPs are given a per capita fee for each patient on their list who lives in an area defined as deprived. In principle such an aim is commendable. In practice the actual method of calculating the payments has been severely criticised (Carr-Hill and Sheldon, 1991; Senior, 1991; Hobbs, 1993). Moreover, payments are unrelated to the quality or quantity of services provided. In fact, some commentators have suggested that deprivation payments act as compensation for GPs in deprived areas who have higher workloads and/or fail to achieve health promotion targets (Lynch, 1994).

Despite these problems, the basic principle of allocating additional resources to areas of high deprivation to reflect the greater level of need is a valid one. What is needed, however, is a much more radical reform, namely the development of a weighted capitation formula to ensure the fair distribution of GPs and related services between areas. One possible way forward might be to develop a need indicator based on data about the characteristics of people who consult their GPs most frequently. Benzeval and Judge (1995) show how this might be done using household survey data and the 1991 census. Comparing their estimate of need to the actual availability of doctors, they found persistent inequalities in access to general practice. Policies need to be developed to tackle such inequities.

If the allocation of resources for FHS remains largely isolated from the distribution of other health and social care services, then promoting greater equity of access will continue to be problematic. For example, it will never be easy to persuade existing GPs to move from one part of the country to another. However, the MPC should begin to use information on the relative needs of different areas more systematically in its decisions about the distribution of new GPs. In addition, more flexible resources, such as cash-limited budgets for practice staff and premises, could be concentrated in areas that are thought to be under-provided in terms of numbers of GPs. However, what would make much more sense is to consider more radical approaches to equitable resource allocation across the whole NHS.

Towards integrated purchasing

Neither of the two main funding streams for local health care provision adequately reflects variations in need. Moreover, there is no guarantee that an area which is deficient in resources in one stream is compensated by more resources for alternative services in another. In fact, the opposite is much more likely; the piecemeal approach to resource allocation therefore almost certainly exacerbates inequalities in access to health care.

Some incremental reforms could be made to the separate funding streams to improve equity of access to health care. But it would be much more satisfactory to find a way of bringing them together into a unified weighted capitation system. This would allow local decision makers to adjust the balance of services in ways that best reflect the opportunities and constraints in their areas.

Recent policy developments could be interpreted as moving in the desired direction – towards integrated purchasing arrangements – by breaking down traditional distinctions between primary and secondary care. During 1994 a number of policy changes were announced that will lead towards a primary care-led NHS. Two major changes are planned. First, it is intended 'to create a new type of health authority to replace existing district and family health services authorities' (NHSE, 1994, p. 1). Secondly, it has been decided to increase 'both the numbers of GPs involved in fundholding and the range of services they can buy' (EL(94)79, para. 4). The expectation is that these changes will facilitate 'a stronger partnership between health authorities and all GPs (fundholders and non-fundholders)' (EL(94)79, para. 2).

The most radical implication of these proposals is that increasing numbers of GPs 'in a locality [will] purchase all hospital and community health service care for their patients' (EL(94)79, para. 5). As this becomes more commonplace the new health authorities will be largely restricted to strategic, monitoring and support roles within the context of developing new partnerships with GPs.

These developments have given rise to fears that crucial aspects of the equity orientation of the NHS will be undermined. First, there is concern that, as health authorities progressively withdraw from direct purchasing, investments in broadly based population interventions directed at communities and groups that are more disadvantaged will be significantly reduced. Secondly, it is not at all clear that adequate data and methodologies are available to allocate resources to fundholders in ways that fully reflect the health care needs of their patients. This could exacerbate the phenomenon of 'cream skimming'; incentives will be created for fundholders to limit care on the grounds of cost rather than appropriateness or even to exclude some patients altogether.

What can be done to guard against these dangers and to ensure that equity considerations are given the priority they demand? The first requirement is that all locally available NHS resources (including hospital care, community-based services and payments to GPs themselves) should be distributed between health authorities on the basis of a comprehensive assessment of total health care needs. If there is a continuing requirement for GPs to be directly involved in purchasing patient care then it is essential that the health authority allocates finance to them in flexible ways that minimise the risks of cream skimming and allows the ring fencing of sufficient resources to promote population-based interventions. The international experience suggests that sophisticated approaches to risk-adjustment capitation are difficult to design and implement, and this implies that decentralised budget initiatives need firm control. A strong health authority committed to and accountable for promoting equity is a minimum requirement for the future. It is essential that enthusiasm for fundholding is not permitted to undermine the responsibilities of health authorities:

for assessing the health care needs of the local population and for developing integrated strategies for meeting those needs across primary and secondary care boundaries.

(EL (94)79, para. 7)

Access to health care services

Even if health care services were distributed between areas in direct proportion to their relative need, it would not automatically result in equal access to health care for all social groups. Health authorities may not always use the resources available to them in the most efficient way to meet the needs of their populations and different social groups may face different barriers to access. For example, facilities may not be located in places that are easy to reach without a car. People may have jobs or caring responsibilities that make it difficult for them, say, to visit surgeries during normal opening times. Health care professionals and users frequently have different social and cultural backgrounds that, if not acknowledged, can hinder effective communication and care.

The purpose of this section of the chapter therefore is twofold. First, to examine the existing evidence about equality of access to health care between different social groups. Secondly, to identify ways in which health care services can be improved to better meet the needs of people in disadvantaged circumstances.

Evidence

The Black Report and other commentators have argued that the least advantaged social groups have poorer access to health services relative to their need than their more advantaged peers. For example, Le Grand (1978) found that, relative to need, professional and managerial groups appeared to receive over 40 per cent more NHS expenditure per capita than those in semi- and unskilled occupations. Collins and Klein, however, disputed this finding on methodological grounds and reported that:

equity in terms of access appears broadly to have been achieved in one crucial aspect at least – that is, once [primary care] *use has been standardised for self-reported morbidity, the remaining variations are not systematically related to social class.*

(1980, p. 1114)

What is not in doubt is that more disadvantaged social groups have higher than average rates of both morbidity and service use. The analytical problem arises in adjusting the one for the other. For example, a more recent paper that takes a different approach from Le Grand suggests that there are no clear-cut differences between income groups in need-adjusted use of services. In some instances, a case can be made that the most affluent people make more use of services than those people with low incomes. For example, Figure 7.1 shows that having standardised for age and sex, people who reported their health as not good in the highest income quintile use 2 per cent more GP services and 17 per cent more in-patient services than those in the lowest. Nevertheless, when a broader range of measures of health status and utilisation are considered, O'Donnell and Propper conclude that 'far from the NHS being pro-rich, there is some inequity in favour of lower income groups' (1991, p. 17).

Despite this powerful assertion of the equity orientation of the NHS, it cannot be assumed that there is no room for improvement. At a local level and in relation to specific services there is clear evidence of a mismatch between the need for and supply of services. For example, in a survey of services for the mental health of children and young people, Kurtz and colleagues (1994) found that area variations in the need for care were positively associated with indices of deprivation and negatively associated with the availability of psychiatrists. More generally, Macintyre suggests that inequalities in access to care:

could influence the distribution of disease or death across social groups at each of three levels of prevention – primary, secondary or tertiary. Preventive procedures, such as immunisation,

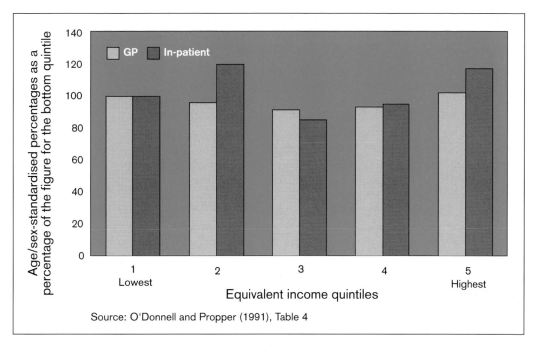

Figure 7.1: Average health care utilisation among adults who reported their health as not good, *General Household Survey,* Great Britain, 1985

could influence the incidence of disease among different social groups if differentially available or used; screening or treatment procedures could influence cure or survival if differentially available, used or effective; and rehabilitation or after-care service could influence the consequences of disease again if differentially available, used, and effective.

(1989, p. 321)

In terms of primary prevention a number of studies have found that individuals from areas with high deprivation have a low uptake of immunisation (Marsh and Channing, 1987; Bennett and Smith, 1992). Perhaps most worryingly, Reading and colleagues (1994) found that when a general programme was introduced to increase the uptake of immunisation, social inequalities widened. Social class gradients have also been found in relation to use of antenatal care, family planning clinics and birth control advice from GPs, with women from manual social classes making less use of these services (Cartwright, 1970). Such differences may be reflected in the higher number of teenage pregnancies and lower levels of abortion among women in disadvantaged circumstances (Smith, 1993). In addition, as Chapter 3 has shown, traditional forms of health education have been less successful with people from disadvantaged environments. More specifically, evidence suggests that there is lower utilisation of health promotion clinics among poorer social and economic groups (Gillam, 1992).

There is also evidence of lower utilisation of screening services among more disadvantaged groups. A number of studies have found lower uptake of general health checks (Pill *et al.,* 1988; Waller *et al.,* 1990), breast cancer screening (French *et al.,* 1982) and cervical screening (Coulter and Baldwin, 1987; Majeed *et al.,* 1994a) among disadvantaged social and economic groups. Women from minority ethnic groups have also been found to have lower rates of cervical smears (McAvoy and Raza, 1988). The impact of such differences on health outcome is difficult to assess. Analysis of the *Longitudinal Study* found lower survival rates among people living in council housing for cancers where a good prognosis would normally be expected. Delay in seeking treatment was believed to be the main contributory factor to these avoidable deaths, although differential treatment, host resistance and other factors were also thought to play a role (Kogevinas *et al.*, 1991).

Evidence that people in disadvantaged circumstances are differentially treated by health care professionals is more difficult to find. In terms of medical consultations, a number of studies have shown that people from the middle classes spent more time on average with their GP than those with working class backgrounds (Buchan and Richardson, 1973; Cartwright and O'Brien, 1976). Cartwright and O'Brien (1976) analysed the content of consultations and showed that people with middle class backgrounds found it easier to communicate with their GP: they discussed more problems, asked more questions and gave more information. Overall, they suggested that 'doctors have a rather less sympathetic and understanding relationship with working-class patients' (p. 92). Blaxter (1984) found that 'referral to specialist care, in relation to presumed need, seems to be biased in favour of social classes I and II' (p. 1967). Other studies have found lower referral rates (Cummins *et al.*, 1981) and lower rates of test ordering (Hartley *et al.*, 1984) per consultation for people from manual social classes. However, both of these studies found that when annual rates were compared the differences between social groups disappeared or were reversed, reflecting the higher number of consultations per year among the more disadvantaged groups.

In terms of acute care, some studies have shown poorer access to services to manage ischaemic heart disease among residents from areas of high deprivation (Majeed *et al.*, 1994b), although others have found no such relationship (Kee *et al.*, 1993). Ben-Shlomo and Chaturvedi (1994) found that although patients from deprived areas consulted their GP more for a number of specific conditions, the relationship between surgical interventions and disadvantage was mixed. Operation rates were positively associated with deprivation for varicose veins, unrelated to deprivation for hernias and gallstones, but negatively associated for hips. There are a number of different possible explanations for results such as these, including systematic differences in GP referral rates or treatment by hospital consultants between social groups.

There is also evidence to suggest that women and older people have poorer access to treatment for heart disease than men or younger groups. For example, having controlled for morbidity, women have been found to have lower rates of angioplasty or coronary artery bypass grafts (Petticrew *et al.*, 1993) and coronary catheterisation and angiography (Kee *et al.*, 1993). Older people have been found to have much more severe symptoms for a longer time period when undergoing coronary angiography than younger people (Elder *et al.*, 1991).

Overall, therefore, there is evidence to support the notion that there are inequalities in access to care, particularly for primary prevention, including personal health promotion, and screening. Much less evidence is available about differences in treatment patterns between social groups, but what there is seems to suggest similar results. The clear implication is that the NHS should devote more effort to assessing the true extent of inequalities in access to care. The next section suggests way in which this might be done.

Monitoring the equity of health care

For a national health service that has equal access for equal need as one of its founding principles, it is disturbing to note how little is known about whether the reality matches the aspiration. It is to be hoped, therefore, that the new role of purchasers will enable and encourage them to focus on equity issues. Purchasers are charged with assessing the health needs of their populations, contracting relevant services for them and evaluating the care received. Current evidence suggests that purchasers are focusing on monitoring efficiency and activity levels (Majeed and Pollock, 1993), but equity considerations should be a more important part of the monitoring process than appears to be the case. Whatever future organisational changes are introduced into the NHS, it is essential that all of its constituent parts – whether purchasers, providers or regulators – do not lose sight of the fact that their primary responsibility is to respond to health care needs in an equitable and non-discriminatory way. Developing the capacity to monitor the implementation of this equity commitment is crucial.

Routine data on hospital activity available in the minimum contract dataset contain patients' demographic information and their postcode. Using postcode information purchasers can link hospital treatment and admission rates to socioeconomic data from the 1991 census. Similarly, FHSAs can link GP activity data with information about the characteristics of the patients in the practice. Such information can be used to map patterns of resource use and service outcomes against the socioeconomic profile of localities. This will enable inequalities in resource allocation and the poor uptake or outcome of services to be identified. Box 7.1 presents a scheme designed by Majeed and colleagues (1994b) to illustrate how this might be done in relation to the treatment of ischaemic heart disease.

Of course, the amount of work required for purchasers to undertake equity audits should not be underestimated. In addition, purchasers and providers need to collaborate to improve the data specification and analysis required to monitor the equity of services, audit the appropriateness of care and feed the results back into the contracting process (Majeed *et al.*, 1994b). Nevertheless, it is essential that such equity audits begin sooner rather than later so that the reality of the NHS's commitment to equal access for equal need can be assessed. In the meantime, it seems reasonable to assume that there are inequalities of access to health care and that new kinds of services should be provided for those who are most disadvantaged.

Improving community-based services

Universal entitlement to health care in Britain on the basis of citizenship should mean that no one is denied access to services. Although we have suggested that some individuals and groups do have barriers to health care, they do not loom as large as those encountered by people who are uninsured in other countries such as the USA. Nevertheless, despite its commitment in principle to universal access on the basis of need, the NHS could do much better to make this a practical reality for people in disadvantaged circumstances by removing or reducing barriers that restrict access to health services.

There are at least three different kinds of barriers – geographic, financial and cultural – that restrict access to health care in the NHS. Much more concerted efforts are required to

Box 7.1: Auditing the equity of access to secondary care

Majeed and colleagues (1994b) have developed a methodology to examine the equity of access to treatment for specific diseases. Their approach involves the development of models of care that identify a number of different stages of treatment for a specific disease. An example for ischaemic heart disease is set out below. At each stage, measures of need, outcome and access can be analysed by the demographic characteristics of patients and the socioeconomic profile of their area of residence. In this example, therefore, access to angiography could be audited by comparing the proportion of admissions from different socioeconomic areas. If differences were found between areas, the purchaser would need to investigate this further to assess whether equality of access to provision was being achieved.

Model of care approach for ischaemic heart disease describing the process of care and measures of need and access

Process of care	Proxy measures of need, access and outcome (analysed by age, sex, geographical area, race)
Access to hospital care	Ratio of admission rates to death rates
Access to angiography	Percentage of admissions investigated
Transfer from angiography to reperfusion treatment	Ratio of number of reperfusions to number of angiographies
Access to reperfusion treatment	Percentage of admissions reperfused
Outcome	Case fatality of in-patients

Source: Majeed *et al.* (1994b), Figure 3

design and deliver appropriate and sensitive services to overcome these problems. We review some of the features of efforts already made that lead in this direction and consider how they might be improved. But first we illustrate how some of the key barriers to access to health care in Britain operate today.

Geographic barriers to care may occur when health care facilities are not located in places that are easy to access by those who most need them. For example, a number of studies have shown that facilities are often located in more affluent areas (Whitehead, 1992). Moreover, people in disadvantaged circumstances who may not have access to a car, tend to be reliant on public transport, which can be expensive, inconvenient and unreliable.

Although the vast majority of NHS services are universally available free at the point of delivery, a number of them impose user charges. Critics argue that such charges reduce demand, particularly among people who are disadvantaged. For example, one recent study has identified a reduction in referrals from opticians for glaucoma following the introduction of a fee for sight tests in 1989 (Laidlaw *et al.*, 1994); the implication being that people in need have been discouraged from having their eyes tested because of the charge. More broadly, differential opportunity costs may act as barriers to access for different social groups. For example, people paid hourly may be reluctant to attend a clinic during working hours. Appointment systems and clinic opening times may be problematic if an individual has caring responsibilities. Even more significantly, people who are homeless or living in poverty may have so many other more pressing demands on their time that attending health care facilities or changing their behaviour is not a priority (Graham 1987; Conway, 1993).

Finally, communication between professionals and users and the provision of information in the health services are often perceived to be poor (Audit Commission, 1994). This may be a particular problem for individuals who have different social and cultural backgrounds from the majority of professionals they encounter, such as minority ethnic groups or those with poor social and economic circumstances. For example, a number of the studies outlined above show how people from manual occupations spend less time and exchange less information with their GP than those with non-manual jobs (Cartwright and O'Brien, 1976). Similarly, there is some evidence to suggest that communication barriers and cultural stereotypes may reduce the quality of care that minority ethnic groups receive (Bowler, 1993).

Health care delivery systems that are committed to pay more than lip service to universal coverage need to find ways of overcoming geographic, financial and cultural barriers to care if they are to achieve equal access for equal need. In many respects this means health services need to place particular emphasis on improving the access of individuals in disadvantaged circumstances. Given the types of barriers health agencies need to over-come, the most appropriate intervention is likely to be the further development of community-based services as these can be more flexible with respect to their location, organisation and delivery.

Traditionally, community-based services have tried to reduce the barriers to access of people who are disadvantaged by targeting services in a variety of ways. At a very general level, many health authorities have developed health profiles, based on local information about the morbidity, mortality and socioeconomic circumstances of areas, to identify neighbourhoods with high levels of health needs (Womersley and McCauley, 1987). For example, Oxford region has worked in this way to target a neighbourhood with poor socioeconomic circumstances prior to identifying priority issues for action with the local community (Root, 1995).

Chapter 3 and Chapter 6 show how initiatives by health services to encourage healthy lifestyles can be sensitive and supportive to people's circumstances in ways that promote positive change. More specifically, in this chapter therefore we focus on the provision of health care services. Health authorities have established a variety of initiatives to target areas or individuals with high needs because of their social and economic circumstances. Box 7.2 describes four initiatives that have approached this issue in different ways.

- Health authorities have frequently provided outreach services in areas of high depriva-tion to make them easier for individuals to access. Such services can often be more flexible and informal and hence less intimidating for users. Box 7.2 describes an outreach scheme for a child health clinic in south London. Similar schemes have been used for people sleeping rough or living in hostels (RCP, 1994; SCOPH, 1994).

- Health professionals may use administrative records to monitor the health care utilisation of people from poor socioeconomic environments and if appropriate make extra efforts to stimulate the use of services. Box 7.2 describes an initiative in Stockton upon Tees to increase the uptake of preventive care in this way.

- Some authorities provide people in disadvantaged circumstances with supplementary services not available to everyone to improve their health. Box 7.2 describes a child accident prevention scheme in Riverside that takes this approach.

Box 7.2: Targeting community-based health services

Targeting services to improve the access to care of individuals in disadvantaged circumstances has been done in a variety of ways. We set out below four initiatives that illustrate these different approaches.

Outreach services
Targeting services to specific areas can make them easier to access for local people and hence reduce barriers to care. One example of this approach was an initiative to improve the uptake of child health services in a deprived area of south London by establishing a clinic in a local community centre (Betts and Betts, 1990). In comparison to the official health centre the community centre was:

- closer both to where people live and to other facilities, such as schools and shops;

- much less formal and institutional, with a cafeteria and play group and other facilities such as a welfare rights unit.

The clinic successfully increased attendance rates, particularly among previous low attenders.

Monitoring the uptake of families in disadvantaged circumstances
One approach to stimulating increased utilisation of health care has been for professionals to use administrative systems to identify and monitor the use of services by families with poor social and economic circumstances. A GP practice in Stockton on Tees set up an initiative to improve the uptake of preventive care, such as the immunisation of children and attendance at well-woman and well-man clinics, among patients from the most deprived neighbourhoods in its catchment area (Marsh and Channing, 1988). First, it audited the medical records of all families on its list who lived on a severely deprived council estate. Information on outstanding treatment was collated by household and attached to the front of the medical record of each member of that household. This enabled the health professionals to raise the matter with any person in the household with whom they came into contact. In addition, a letter was sent to each household highlighting the treatment required by each person. As a result many patients made appointments to receive the outstanding care. When all else failed, one of the GPs and a health visitor arranged to visit the family at home and carry out the necessary care.

- Finally, many authorities have recognised the particular barriers that minority ethnic groups may encounter when using mainstream services either because of language or cultural differences. Box 7.2 describes linkworker and advocate schemes that have tried to overcome these problems.

These kinds of initiatives have much to commend them. At the very least they demonstrate a commitment to identify and respond to needs that are too frequently overlooked. At the same time, many of them suffer from a number of problems that need to be addressed if a broader and more appropriate approach to improving access to care for all is to be achieved. First, such initiatives have tended to be grafted on to existing services in an

Box 7.2: continued

Statistically significant increases in prevention rates were achieved among this specific population. In fact, for some interventions people with poor socioeconomic circumstances achieved higher coverage rates than the more affluent patients. However, substantial additional administration was required to operate the scheme, highlighting the fact that often significant extra resources are required to achieve similar coverage among the most disadvantaged groups. Moreover, forcing a professionally determined agenda on people in this way may be inappropriate. There is a fine dividing line between encouragement to take up a service and undue pressure, verging on bullying. High ethical standards with respect for personal integrity need to be maintained.

Supplementary services

One example of the health advantages to be obtained from the provision of supplementary services to families in disadvantaged circumstances relates to accident prevention. A case-control study was set up in a deprived area of Riverside to accompany a national television campaign on child accident prevention. The intervention group was given a booklet accompanying the programme and received a visit from a health visitor to discuss hazards in their homes and how they could be reduced. The control group was just told about the television programme. Both groups watched the programme to a similar extent. However, the intervention group were over six times more likely than the control group to have made changes to the physical environment of their homes to reduce the risk of accidents (Colver *et al.*, 1982).

Linkworker and advocate schemes

Extra resources may also be used to provide more appropriate services for specific social groups. For example, one increasingly common strategy adopted by health care providers is the use of linkworkers or advocates. Such schemes have mainly been employed in relation to South Asian women and maternity care. The role of linkworkers is to interpret, explain the health care system and 'generally act as a bridge between the … women and the health care professionals' (Hicks and Hayes, 1991, p. 90). Evaluations of such services have shown increased use of care: one authority increased uptake of antenatal services by 50 per cent (Bahl, 1990). However, linkworker schemes have been criticised for ignoring the social and racial context of the women's lives and attempting to change the behaviour of minority groups towards that of the majority (Smaje, 1995). Advocate services, on the other hand, act as watchdogs for their clients' interests, and in City and Hackney – where one such scheme is in operation – they appear to have had a positive effect on perinatal outcomes (Parsons and Day, 1992).

unsatisfactory way. They have to be more fully integrated so that the commitment to equity they embody can inculcate the whole health care delivery system. This is particularly important in terms of improving communication between users and professionals. There is relatively little work on how this might be done, although a limited start was recently made by the Audit Commission (1994) in a report that outlines how to improve communication in hospitals. Such a practical focus needs to be applied to all user–professional communication, with particular emphasis being given to the needs of different social groups.

More fundamentally, special schemes of the kind we have described have tended to impose a professional view of individuals' needs, the appropriate service response and the anticipated outcomes. Such behaviour runs the real risk that service providers will seem to be critical of families who 'fail to use services' or be perceived as trying to get people to fit into traditional forms of service delivery rather than being sensitive to individuals' own perceptions and circumstances. Many providers are therefore developing new approaches to service delivery which empower clients in ways that enable them to define their own needs and outcomes, and help them to design services that are appropriate to their lives.

Empowerment

Empowerment of both communities and individuals should be an important part of policies that aim to tackle inequalities in health. Empowering communities to identify their own needs and priorities for action is vital if health authorities are to tackle the issues of real concern to their most disadvantaged populations. At the same time, it is essential to enable individuals to take more control over their lives and hence improve their health. We set out below an illustrative example of each approach: first, a rapid appraisal system for involving the community in decision making in a cost-effective way; and secondly, the Newpin project which aims to empower women through peer support networks.

The NHS as a whole must encourage a much more widespread and genuine commitment by health authorities to empower local communities to define their health and social needs, and develop strategies and tactics to meet them. One way of doing this is through rapid appraisal techniques, which are 'an approach to understanding the health needs of urban communities, which strengthens the principles of equity, participation and multisectoral co-operation' (Ong et al., 1991, p. 910).

The key features of rapid appraisal are that a team should be formed involving people from various local organisations to collect information from existing written records, the opinions of a range of informants and their own observations about the neighbourhood. Such information collection is based on the concept of 'triangulation', i.e. data from one source can be checked and validated by two other sources. The informants should be chosen because of their knowledge of the local community and may include teachers, the police, health and social care workers, local authority employees, councillors, voluntary leaders, clergy, shopkeepers and postmen, as well as various local interest groups. Once areas of concern have been identified, the information is fed back to the community in order for them to identify priorities for action. Plans are then drawn up in consultation with the community about how improvements can be made. For example, an expanded primary care team carried out a rapid appraisal in Dumbiedykes, a small council estate in

Edinburgh, as the first step in identifying and meeting local needs. As a result a number of local priorities were identified and some improvements in services were implemented. These included routing a bus through the estate; creating dog-free zones; establishing a mental health group and citizen advice and local councillor sessions in the local community centre, as well as making the local GP surgery more responsive to user needs. Croydon has also used this approach in the initiative outlined in Box 7.4 (p. 121).

Even if serious efforts are made to identify and take account of the views of the community, it is still important to ensure that services are delivered in non-patronising ways. In short, service delivery systems as well as needs assessment exercises must promote the empowerment of individuals. One example of such an initiative designed to prevent family breakdowns by empowering women through the use of trained peers is the Newpin project. Newpin (new parent infant network) is a centre-based support and befriending scheme that uses social support and personal development to empower women and raise their self-esteem. It combines a network of women in similar circumstances with a drop-in centre and creche. Women may refer themselves or are referred by a professional to the scheme. After an assessment by a co-ordinator, each woman is teamed up with a 'befriender' who introduces them to the network and provides them with support. Women may choose to take a development programme which combines group therapy for self-development with classes on topics ranging from life events to sociological issues. Having taken this course, the women can take on the role of befrienders themselves. A Department of Health funded evaluation compared women in the Newpin scheme with women in similar circumstances from a nearby area. There was a significant improvement in the psychiatric state of women who were involved in the scheme for between 7 and 12 months. In addition, there were improvements in their self-esteem and feelings of control over their lives and their ability to anticipate the needs of their children (Cox et al., 1991). One problem in the past with the initiative has been its high drop-out rate. Cox and colleagues found that 30 per cent of women did not sustain a significant involvement in the scheme. Moreover, a subsequent evaluation by the Social Science Research Unit (1994) found that half of the women referred to Newpin never joined the network. Clearly, such high drop-out rates are of concern to any potential purchaser of such services. Nevertheless, Newpin's commitment to evaluation is to be commended since it demonstrates the contribution that initiatives aimed at empowering and supporting individuals can make to improving the health of people in disadvantaged circumstances.

Overview

It would be just as wrong to exaggerate the difficulties in gaining access to health care faced by some people in contemporary Britain as it would be to ignore them. Access to health services cannot be taken for granted, especially in the most disadvantaged communities. There is still much to be done to ensure that services are provided in appropriate locations, that user charges do not deter people from expressing legitimate needs and that cultural diversity is not ignored. There have been some attempts to deal with these and related issues, but relatively speaking they remain few and far between. What is more, some of them have occasionally been misguided either in design or implementation or both. Genuine empowerment is the key for the future. People must be involved in helping to identify their own needs, and services must be provided in ways that users themselves recognise as legitimate. If the NHS starts to behave more widely in these kinds of ways then the number of people who have been effectively excluded from care will be reduced. But it must be recognised that any serious efforts to respond to users' views about the health risks they face will go beyond the scope of the NHS itself. In the next section therefore we turn to consider how the NHS can influence the wider determinants of people's health.

The wider agenda

Given that inadequate access to health services makes only a relatively minor contribution to the observed inequalities in health in a country such as Britain, it is sometimes assumed that the NHS has a correspondingly minor role to play in tackling the inequalities caused by factors outside the health sector. Nothing could be further from the truth. The fact is that the health sector should have a major part in encouraging the development of an equity orientation across the whole range of public policies that have an impact on health.

For a number of reasons, the health sector is in a pivotal position as far as others are concerned. First, there is a wealth of experience and expertise among health professionals in measuring the link between health status and a variety of indicators of socioeconomic circumstances. Secondly, it is at the door of the health sector that the health damage caused by other public and private policies is presented. The health sector is therefore in a key position to monitor the effects on health of social and economic policies and to do what it can to ameliorate them. Thirdly, there is the question of credibility. If the health sector is not concerned with inequalities in health, other sectors can hardly be expected to take the issue seriously. It is vital, therefore, that the Department of Health and local purchasers take the lead and provide a driving force if any purposeful strategy in this area is to be achieved. This section looks at equity-oriented health policy, first at the national level and then in relation to local agencies.

National action

Clearly, this report argues for taking social inequalities in health seriously. The problem is seen as one of the biggest challenges in current health policy in this country. Urgent action is needed now in two key areas:

- the formulation of health policy with specific reference to inequalities and a commitment to take action on them, acknowledged, for example, in information gathering, health impact assessment and target setting;
- multisectoral action, with the development of mechanisms for setting up equity-oriented policy across government departments.

There is a clear role for the Department of Health to take in these areas, but progress to date has been patchy.

Equity-oriented health policy

For over ten years there have been calls for a co-ordinated national strategy for health that explicitly recognises the existence of inequalities in health and shows commitment to tackling them. Until recently, these calls appeared to fall on deaf ears; however, attitudes have changed rapidly in the 1990s. National health promotion strategies have been drawn up, first in Wales (Health Promotion Authority for Wales, 1990) and then for England (Cm 1986, 1992), Scotland (Scottish Office, 1992) and Northern Ireland (DHSSNI, 1992). The Welsh strategy is undoubtedly the most advanced in the UK in terms of acknowledging inequalities and advocating concerted action to reduce them.

> *Affirmative action is needed to enable the disadvantaged to reach their full health potential.*
> *... by focusing health promotion activity more effectively it should be possible to make proportionately greater improvements over time within groups that are more in need.*
>
> (Health Promotion Authority for Wales, 1990, pp. 7–8)

Likewise, the Northern Ireland strategy, while mainly being restricted to health and social services, puts the promotion of greater equity in health at the forefront of its stated aims:

> *within Northern Ireland there is clear evidence of inequalities in health status. ... In order to provide an equitable response to need, it is important for such inequalities to be identified and addressed.*
>
> (DHSSNI, 1992, p. 32)

With the English and Scottish documents, although they signal a welcome move towards wider health promotion, they have yet to make such a commitment and formulate associated policy. Nevertheless, one recent development holds promise for the future: in May 1994 a sub-group of the Chief Medical Officer's *Health of the Nation* Working Group was established to examine variations in health (DoH, 1994b). Could this be the beginning of more positive moves to tackle inequalities in health in England?

Whatever the level of emerging interest in equity issues, a more systematic strategy is needed for monitoring and disseminating information on socioeconomic inequalities in health. This entails going beyond the collection of data useful for the planning of health service delivery, to data of potential use to other relevant agencies, such as those concerned with housing and employment, and to the general public to enable them to make informed choices. It also means collecting information on the major causes of health problems such as individuals' living and working conditions and restrictions on their lifestyles, in addition to health status *per se*. In guidelines on measuring inequalities in health, WHO recommends the addition of socioeconomic information to existing health datasets, and correspondingly, the addition of health measures to existing social and economic statistics, to avoid setting up expensive new systems if possible (Kunst and Mackenbach, 1994).

In many respects the UK already has some of the most sophisticated monitoring systems in the world capable of registering the existence of inequalities in health. For example, the routine recording of occupation on death certificates and the linkage of health and census data have helped in identifying health differentials in the population. However, routine population surveys, patient records from general practice and existing hospital statistics could all be improved, particularly in monitoring the contribution of risk factors and health hazards by socioeconomic status.

There is concern that we may be going backwards rather than forwards in some aspects of information gathering. With the introduction of the NHS reforms and the creation of a less unified service some information is no longer collected centrally – for example, some hospital statistics and activity directed into the private sector from primary care. More generally, since the beginning of the 1980s, cuts have been made to the collection of national health and social statistics, and there have been regular calls to narrow rather than widen the range of information collected, following the famous 'Rayner principle' that:

> *information should not be collected primarily for publication. It should be collected primarily because government needs it for its own business.*
>
> (Cabinet Office, 1980, p. 17)

In the light of these developments, there has to be a renewed commitment to maintaining valuable datasets, and not only in areas where health services can make an impact.

Health impact assessment is another key aspect of monitoring at a national level. Many policies have, to a greater or lesser degree, an impact on health. It is essential therefore that as policies develop the consequences for health are assessed and, where appropriate, taken into account. The methodology for this is in its infancy, but some countries, such as The Netherlands and Sweden, have made a start. The health sector in the UK has the responsibility for putting concerted effort into developing a methodology and promoting consideration of the health impact of policy making in other sectors. A promise to this effect was made in the English health strategy document *The Health of the Nation* (Cm 1986, 1992). Whether any progress has been made on this promise is hard to tell, as no further reports have been forthcoming. A crucial point when development work does start is to ensure that the impact on the health of the most vulnerable in society is measured.

Having equity-oriented targets should also help to keep the national focus on reducing inequalities in health. In the health strategy for Wales, inequalities were clearly acknowledged and some of the detailed targets that were set explicitly aimed to reduce them. For example, for infant mortality a target was set to reduce the mortality rate to less than 7 per 1,000 live births in all six social classes (i.e. I, II, IIIn-m, IIIm, IV, V), with three groups achieving this by 1995 and all groups by the year 2000 (Health Promotion Authority for Wales, 1990).

Targets of this nature, which recognise existing differentials in health across social groups, are an essential component of a health strategy.

Multisectoral action

One over-riding question concerning action at a national level is: how can a Secretary of State for Health, worthy of the name, promote healthy public policies across all spheres of government?

The Black Report back in 1980 stressed the need for wide-ranging action to tackle inequalities in health in its recommendations for interdepartmental machinery in the Cabinet Office to co-ordinate the administration of health-related policies (recommendation 36), and for equivalent local mechanisms to be developed (Townsend and Davidson, 1982). Under *The Health of the Nation* white paper a ministerial cabinet committee has been set up covering eleven government departments, to develop and implement the strategy. Unfortunately, to date the committee has kept a low profile, and it is difficult to gain information on its activities, although the impression given is that inequalities in health have not been prominent on the agenda. The committee urgently needs to turn its attention to promoting multisectoral action and co-ordination to tackle inequalities in health.

There is the more fundamental question of whether such a committee with the existing structure could overcome the obstacles to effective interdepartmental action. There needs to be a mechanism capable of ensuring a health input into the Treasury, for instance, as a key department that spans several sectors. Many of the policy options discussed in earlier chapters of this report depend for their success on the way the Treasury accounting systems deal with expenditure and where it attributes costs and benefits. For example, in relation to healthy housing, spending now on upgrading the thermal efficiency of existing housing, starting with the homes of families with low incomes, would have a positive impact on health, on fuel poverty and on national energy consumption, as well as boosting jobs in the construction industry. It has been calculated that the cost of a ten-year programme of such housing improvements would be covered by the price of the energy saved in the process (House of Lords, 1991; Smith, 1994). However, these costs and benefits are not at present considered in a unitary way by the Treasury. The capital costs are included in the PSBR, while the savings in energy, health and social security expenditure are not entered into the equation. As there are heavy restrictions on public sector expenditure, essential work which makes health and economic sense in the long run is being prohibited (Boardman, 1994).

Mechanisms need to be put in place to overcome such barriers to effective multisectoral action as a matter of priority.

Local purchasers

To complement national action there is a substantial role for local purchasers in developing a strategic framework for tackling inequalities in health within their localities. If current inequalities in the experience of health and illness are to be effectively addressed, it is important that local health agencies build equity as a guiding principle into a strategic framework for the commissioning process. Only in this way will the pursuit of equity become a central as opposed to a marginal component of their work.

Within such a framework there are three main areas of action where purchasers need to make progress: information gathering, preventing and ameliorating ill health, and working with others to change wider social and economic policy. These are highlighted in Box 7.3. In all this work, the existing commitment of local authority staff and of voluntary agencies needs to be acknowledged – some have been attempting to tackle the root causes of inequalities in health for far longer than many from the health care sector as such.

Monitoring and disseminating

As suggested in Box 7.3, purchasers have an important role to play in collecting information relevant to health inequalities in their locality. This includes the assessment of the local impact of social and economic policies on health and the dissemination of that information to local and national policy makers.

Box 7.3: Responding to inequalities in health: what can local purchasers do?

Monitoring and disseminating

- Monitor determinants of health such as unemployment, poverty and poor housing and related ill health in the locality.

- Co-operate with local authorities and voluntary agencies for the more accurate collection of information on these matters.

- Assess the impact of local and national policies on the health of the most vulnerable sections of the population.

- Disseminate the information gathered both inside and beyond the NHS.

Preventing and ameliorating health damage

- Commission mainstream services that provide appropriate social support for all families living in disadvantaged circumstances.

- Commission counselling services to help prevent a decline in mental health following unemployment and other traumatic life events.

- Fund initiatives to encourage the uptake of welfare benefits.

- Create opportunities for people experiencing disadvantage to meet together for mutual support.

- Ensure that, as an employer, the NHS improves the working conditions of its workforce.

Stimulating policy change beyond the NHS

- Participate in the development of interagency health strategies.

- Raise awareness of issues among local agencies and communities.

- Fund community development programmes that help local people participate in decision making.

- Encourage the development of local policies that help people escape poverty and unemployment.

- Play an advocacy role to national agencies.

Purchasers' information systems need to be extended to monitor the level and distribution of factors such as poverty, unemployment and poor housing and related ill health in neighbourhoods. There must also be mechanisms for feeding such information into the commissioning process and to the community itself, so that these factors can be taken into account when targeting responses and resources to those most in need. This requires much closer co-operation than previously with local authorities and voluntary agencies to avoid wasteful duplication of effort in the collection of information.

Such approaches are beginning to be developed in some places. For example, in the new North West Regional Health Authority a common framework and databases have been developed to look at several different dimensions of inequalities – the wider determinants, personal risk factors, health status and access to services. A small-area database provides information on disk to all seventeen purchasing areas in the region, to help them produce more detailed local analyses within the context of regional patterns (North West Regional Health Authority, 1994a; b). Such small-area analyses allow policies to tackle inequalities in health to be based on an assessment of activity in every area, relative to levels of need and provision, rather than focusing only on the poorest areas.

Interesting experiments in identifying work-related illness in primary care settings are also taking place around the country. For example, in Sheffield and Birmingham, occupational health workers are employed to interview patients about their occupational histories when they visit their GPs. As well as giving individual advice on workplace rights, the database on patients is used to look at patterns of illness and to relate diseases to specific industries or hazards in the locality.

Preventing and ameliorating health damage

A major task for local purchasers is to help prevent or ameliorate the ill health caused by socioeconomic factors. Some suggestions as to how they might do this are given in Box 7.3. Purchasers should be aware of changes in the local social and economic infrastructure and develop initiatives to counter their health-damaging effects. For example, health agencies can be proactive in supporting people made redundant when local industries close. This might include commissioning targeted counselling services; providing appropriate social support for families experiencing hardship; and creating opportunities for people to meet together for mutual support. Further examples of this approach can be found in Chapter 3, both in terms of social support of individuals and community development initiatives.

Health care professionals can also try to intervene to improve the social and economic circumstances of their patients by, for example, establishing initiatives to encourage the uptake of welfare benefits. This might be done by funding welfare rights advice in general practice settings or by training health service staff in the social security benefits available. In Birmingham, family health services authorities have funded schemes to give benefit advice in general practice health promotion clinics. In Bristol, a joint health authority/social services project has been funded in deprived parts of the city. Tens of thousands of pounds in unclaimed and refused benefits have been gained by patients as a result (Richards, 1990; Paris and Player, 1993).

The NHS can, of course, also directly improve the working conditions for its own employees, many of whom are on low pay and experiencing highly stressful working environments.

Stimulating policy change beyond the NHS

Stimulating policy change beyond the NHS requires local purchasers to raise awareness of inequalities in health among local agencies and communities, and to participate in the development of interagency health strategies wherever possible.

Local purchasers have been active in encouraging the development of policies that help people escape from poverty, unemployment and other socioeconomic hazards. Although much depends on national policy, a useful contribution can be made by efforts at a more local level. Health authorities have even been known to create jobs and work for local people who are unemployed by skilful use of resources from outside sources (Smith, 1987).

However, much more attention needs to be paid to how joint initiatives by local agencies can be linked into each agency's main programmes of work, rather than remaining on the periphery. Currently, there is a tendency for a few joint projects to be set up in each area in a piecemeal fashion, sometimes under the banner of 'healthy alliances', and predominantly involving health education at the individual or community level. In all regions of the country, good examples can be found of joint projects on specific issues in some of the more disadvantaged areas. But for the NHS to help tackle the wider determinants of inequalities in health effectively, there needs to be a health input into some of the main functions of local organisations, such as housing, education and economic development. Linkages are already being made to mainstream policy making in this way by some health agencies.

For example, Box 7.4 describes how three different cities have developed integrated policy making between the local authorities and health agencies to tackle the wider determinants of health. Four key themes are shown to emerge.

- Structural links are required at the most senior levels of the organisations in order for effective joint strategies to be agreed. This enables the health agencies to have a direct link into the implementation of wider policies that have an impact on health.

- The policy-making process includes a wide range of members of both health and local authorities, as well as voluntary organisations, community and business groups.

- Assessments of needs and priorities are conducted with the full participation of the local community.

- The resulting strategies cover a broad range of local policies including housing, education, environment, health services, transport and benefit uptake.

In all three cities, the health agencies concerned stress that they see that the most valuable outcome of such joint working is the increased recognition of the importance of health as an issue when local policies outside the NHS are formulated. Joint initiatives such as these should be established at the local level across the UK so that effective interagency strategies can be developed to tackle inequalities in health.

Overview

The Department of Health and local purchasers must take the lead in promoting policies to tackle inequalities in health. At a national level leadership is required to develop a multisectoral equity-orientated health strategy. At a local level purchasers need to develop information strategies and joint infrastructures with other organisations to tackle the wider determinants of inequalities in health.

Conclusion

A central assumption of this book is the belief that health care provision is not the most important way of tackling inequalities in health successfully. However, the NHS does have a contribution to make. Its first responsibility is to ensure greater equity of access to care by distributing resources in relation to needs and removing barriers that inhibit effective use of services. Secondly, all parts of the NHS have an obligation to promote a greater orientation towards equity and the development of healthy public policies both nationally and locally. We summarise below a number of key requirements that are needed to achieve these objectives.

First, we have acknowledged that the current resource allocation systems help to redress historic inequities, but further reforms are needed. All health care resources at the local level must be more closely linked to the relative need for them. In addition, the introduction of primary care-led purchasing must be taken forward with great care. The scope for closer integration of primary and secondary care is welcome, but new forms of fundholding must not allow cream skimming to flourish or to crowd out population-based investments in new community services. Whatever the merits of decentralised budgets that facilitate more flexible responses to individual patients, we are convinced that there will continue to be a critically important role for an all-purpose local health authority charged with the primary responsibility for identifying and meeting the needs of the whole population.

Secondly, given the historic and enduring commitment to ensuring equal access for equal need, it is vital that the NHS makes much greater efforts to assess whether this is achieved by conducting equity audits of both primary and secondary care. Moreover, barriers to services should be identified and dealt with whenever and however they occur. One approach that would do much to broaden the reach of health care to under-served groups is the development of more effective community-based services that empower individuals and communities to assess their own needs and develop appropriate service responses.

Finally, the NHS needs to take an active leadership role in developing policy responses to the wider determinants of health in ways that promote equity. At the national level mechanisms should be put in place to facilitate interdepartmental co-ordination and co-operation, to set and achieve equity-orientated health targets and to assess the health impact of all public policies. At the local level health authorities need to work with local agencies and their communities to identify priorities across the range of services that might reduce inequalities in health.

Box 7.4: Integrated policy making

Liverpool healthy city 2000: from project to integrated policy making
Liverpool was one of the first cities to be enrolled in the WHO healthy cities project in 1986. Although many innovative programmes were developed under its umbrella, the project faced criticisms that it was a marginal and limited initiative divorced from mainstream decision making in the city. To overcome these criticisms the initiative was restructured in 1993 to ensure that it was linked into the main policy-making activities of the city council and local health agencies by using the joint consultative committee (JCC). In effect, Liverpool no longer has a healthy city 'project' as a distinct entity, instead it has become integrated into planning for the health of the city.

The JCC oversees a joint public health team that consists of senior officers from both authorities, including, from the council, the directors of housing, social services, environmental services and education, and from the health sector, the director of public health and the assistant chief executive, as well as representatives from the business and community groups. Through this mechanism, the health sector has greater influence and input into policy making on such issues as housing, transport, and community regeneration within the city.

For example, a housing and health task group has been set up that aims 'to ensure healthy housing for all Liverpool people' and to achieve this, it is currently engaged in:

- research projects on housing conditions and health;

- promoting the availability of grants for improving the energy efficiency of homes;

- physical and environmental improvements to the public housing in the worst conditions;

- continued action on fuel poverty by replacing ineffective warm air heating systems;

- action to reduce lead poisoning by a programme of lead mains replacement;

- strengthening inspection and enforcement activities to deal with the particularly hazardous conditions faced by people living in houses of multiple occupancy;

- examining the needs of people who are homeless and improving their access to health services;

- supporting welfare benefit take-up schemes.

Glasgow: encouraging participation
As in Liverpool, the Glasgow healthy city project has been deliberately structured to link into the policy-making committees of local government and health boards. Joint efforts have included:

- detailed mapping of socioeconomic conditions and health to feed into the planning process;

- research in conjunction with the OECD to monitor the impact on health of the various housing improvement programmes in different parts of the city;

- extensive welfare benefits campaigns extending into primary health care settings, with evaluated experiments in providing benefits advice in GP surgeries, and welfare rights guides supplied to every GP, health visitor and hospital consultant;

- a programme to empower people to participate more in action to reduce inequalities in health.

Box 7.4: continued

This last initiative involves the Scottish Office, health boards, district and regional councils, voluntary sector, economic development and housing organisations in a scheme funded under the urban programme. Following a city-wide assessment, eight areas of multiple deprivation have been identified. Joint community health needs assessments identified perceived problems in each area, predominantly poverty, fuel poverty, poor physical environment, housing repairs, inadequate access to health services, poor availability of food, neighbourhood problems associated with drug abuse and the lack of provision for the needs of children. In each area, the programme trains residents who were previously unemployed as community health workers with community development skills. They are then employed in their own locality to train further health volunteers, create support groups, and build up a community-led health information service, to actively encourage participation on the priorities the communities themselves perceive as the most pressing.

Multi-agency think-tanks in Croydon

In Croydon think-tanks have been set up in two different areas under the umbrella of the joint consultative committee, to look at the causes of poor health and to propose actions to improve health. Their membership is drawn from the council and the health commissioning agency, the community NHS trust, GPs, schools, voluntary and minority ethnic organisations. As well as an examination of research evidence, a multitiered consultation was undertaken with the communities including the use of rapid appraisal techniques, public meetings in every ward, a leaflet with tear-off slip for comments delivered to every household, social surveys and focus groups.

As a result a strategy for action is being developed that includes:

- the provision of more childcare for people who wish to train or work;

- improved public transport to the town centre and in local areas;

- housing and environmental improvement programmes;

- better facilities for community development;

- adult education and training services;

- benefit take-up campaigns;

- economic redevelopment;

- better joint planning of health and social services locally.

Reducing inequalities in health and promoting equality of access to health services' have been built into the 1995–96 purchasing intentions of the Croydon Health Commissioning Agency and joint finance from health and local authorities has been earmarked for such schemes.

Sources: Personal communications from Peter Flynn (Liverpool); Andrew Lyon and David Black (Glasgow); Ted Williams (Croydon)

CHAPTER **8**

Unfinished business

Michaela Benzeval, Ken Judge and Margaret Whitehead

The main aim of this book is to contribute to the process of developing a practical agenda for tackling inequalities in health in Britain. In attempting to do this we have built upon the extensive research literature that for many years has documented the extent and nature of social variations in health. We have identified existing interventions that could address specific aspects of the problem, and reviewed a number of possible innovations across different spheres of health and social policy that we believe merit careful consideration. In doing so, however, we are only too well aware that we have not been able to consider every policy option that deserves attention. In this final chapter, therefore, we mention briefly those topics that participants at the Ditchley Park seminar felt had been most neglected.

A significant concern expressed by participants was that we had inadvertently perpetuated biases within the inequalities research tradition which, because of data limitations, has focused excessive attention on the health experiences of white males of working age. We acknowledge the validity of this unease, and emphasise below that in future much more attention should be given to inequalities among women, older people and minority ethnic groups.

The second main concern was that although the policy areas selected for detailed scrutiny – housing, income maintenance, smoking and access to health care – are very important, they might not represent a sufficiently comprehensive agenda for tackling inequalities. In particular, a strong conviction was expressed that the causes and consequences of unemployment demand a higher profile. In short, new policies are needed that better prepare all sections of the community for the life of work and enable more parents to combine employment with child rearing, as well as providing services that respond more appropriately when people lose their jobs. We also illustrate some of the policy options that have been canvassed recently in each of these areas. These are not policies that would necessarily be endorsed by the Ditchley Park participants or by ourselves. However, they are intended to provide some indication of the kinds of choices that could be made.

Neglected population groups

One of the main reasons why inequalities in health in Britain have been so well documented is the fact that information about occupation has been linked to vital statistics such as birth and death registration for such a long period of time. Indicators of social class and socioeconomic group, which are derived from occupational classifications, have proved in the past to be powerful discriminators of the material circumstances of different sections of the population. But extensive social change since the Second World War – which has witnessed a rapid ageing of the population, substantial immigration and the transform-ation of the position of women in the labour market – has reduced the utility of social class as a reliable indicator of socioeconomic circumstances for the whole population. As the BMA has suggested:

> *social class is probably becoming a poorer measure of socioeconomic status than in the past, as home ownership, second incomes, single parenthood and unemployment cut across the traditional relationship between husband's occupation and family resources.*

(1987, p. 7)

Of course, substantial social class related gradients in terms of health experiences can still be identified. Almost without exception, for example, non-manual groups have better health and longer life expectancy than manual ones. The problem is that such social class-based analyses are most appropriate for white males of working age. Social class is a much poorer predictor of the socioeconomic circumstances of women outside the labour market, of older people and of minority ethnic groups. This is because:

- women cannot be analysed as a single group in terms of class because a significant proportion of those of working age do not have an occupation;

- the current socioeconomic status of older people may bear little relationship to their past occupation, which usually determines their class status;

- the occupations of minority ethnic groups may not represent their material circum-stances in the same way as the majority population. For example, 'many self-employed South Asian people who would be occupationally classified into higher classes have a lifestyle more akin to that of lower classes' (Smaje, 1995, p. 83), even if one disregards the possibility that they may also suffer from racial discrimination.

It is important to remember, however, that such groups are of growing significance. If they are neglected, for whatever reason, then judgements about the size and nature of inequalities run the risk of being seriously biased. For example, Judge and Benzeval (1993) have shown that the failure to include the children of lone mothers who are economically inactive – a group which is larger than either social class I or V – in analyses of inequalities in childhood mortality substantially underestimates the extent of the problem.

The point to emphasise is that the difficulties of measuring the socioeconomic circumstances of women, older people or minority ethnic groups, should not disguise the fact that members of each group do experience substantial disadvantages that are relevant to any analysis of health inequalities. Given more time and space, it ought to be possible to outline a package of policy options which would improve the health of these relatively disadvantaged groups of the population. However, that is not the purpose of this report where we have chosen to focus our primary attention on specific types of intervention. Here we simply want to highlight the fact that the historic focus on evidence of inequalities among white males of working age, and to a lesser extent children, cannot capture the full extent of the problem in contemporary Britain. We can do no more here than briefly elaborate these points, but we are in no doubt that they merit closer investigation and a higher research priority in the future.

Women

It is well known that women live longer than men. However, it is important not to be misled by this since in many respects women actually have worse health in terms of morbidity. Three reasons have been advanced for this. First, that women's excess morbidity is biologically determined, associated with menstruation and the menopause. Secondly, that women's poor health is a consequence of their social position in what remains a largely patriarchal society. Finally, that the observed differences between men and women are an artefact of gender-based variations in perceptions of illness. On balance, the research evidence suggests that the first and third explanations cannot account for more than part of the excess morbidity. It is important therefore to emphasise the significance of the social determinants of women's health.

The socioeconomic circumstances of women are often difficult to identify as they are frequently hidden in more general analyses, which either focus on the family as the unit of interest (Millar and Glendinning, 1992) or use measures of social status that are inadequate, such as occupational class. For example, 36 per cent of women of working age could not be allocated an occupational classification of their own from the information reported in the 1991 census (Benzeval *et al.*, 1995). To overcome this problem, many studies analyse married women's health status by their husband's occupation and single women by their own. As a result:

> *meaningful comparisons cannot be made between women in different marital status categories. ... One consequence of these deficiencies is that the effect on women's health of their social circumstances is given little attention when health inequalities are discussed.*
> (Moser *et al.*, 1990b, p. 146)

Even though measures of social class are not very helpful at characterising the socioeconomic circumstances of all women it would be a grave mistake to ignore the fact that in many respects poverty and disadvantage are gender issues. There is now compelling evidence that poverty among women in the 1990s:

> *is a consequence of the gender division of labour, which assigns their primary role to the home and the primary role of men to the labour market. This division has profound consequences for the situation of women in the labour market, for their treatment within social welfare systems and for their status and power within the family.*
> (Millar and Glendinning, 1992, p. 5)

Lewis and Piachaud (1992) have demonstrated that this results in women being over-represented among both workers with low pay and people dependent on benefits. For example:

- in the 1980s, women accounted for 42 per cent of the economically active population but received only 26 per cent of total earnings;
- in 1989, 60 per cent of income support recipients were women.

Furthermore, even when total family income may appear to be adequate, it is not always equally distributed: women may be living in poverty when other family members are not. Moreover, it is generally women who have to manage the resources to maintain and provide for the family, adding to the stress that women experience as a result of poverty (Graham, 1993a).

What does this mean for women's health? As Fox and Benzeval showed in Chapter 2, when appropriate measures of socioeconomic status are employed inequalities in women's health are no less prevalent than they are among men. For example, women living in local authority housing with no access to a car have standardised mortality and limiting long-standing illness ratios that are 1.8 times higher than those of women in owner-occupied housing with a car; for men the corresponding ratios are 1.6 for mortality and 2 for long-standing illness (Goldblatt, 1990b; Moser *et al.*, 1990b; Arber, 1991).

Another important reason for acknowledging the significance of inequalities in health among women is that there are gender differences in the way in which health is affected by deprivation. For example, an analysis of the *Survey of Londoners' Living Standards* found that although both men and women in disadvantaged circumstances reported poorer health status, the relative importance of material and social circumstances was reversed. Men appeared to suffer more ill health as a result of poor material circumstances, whereas for women social deprivation appeared to be more important (Benzeval *et al.*, 1992). However, this kind of research is very much in its infancy and it would certainly be wrong to assume that material deprivation is not associated with poor health among women. For example, Popay and Bartley (1993) report that the physical conditions of work in both formal employment and the home are correlated with women's health.

The critical point to emphasise here is that measures of socioeconomic status need to embrace the experience of women as well as men. In addition, much more research is required to understand social inequalities in health among women, in order to design appropriate policy interventions.

Older people

Many people over retirement age are subject to considerable social and economic disadvantage. In 1991 the median income of pensioners was approximately two-thirds that of non-pensioners. Moreover, there are sharp disparities in income between different groups of pensioners. For example, in 1989, individuals with occupational pensions had incomes over 50 per cent higher than those without. A significant proportion of pensioners – 40 per cent of people under 75 and 55 per cent of people over 75 – do not have occupational pensions (Hancock and Weir, 1994).

What does this mean for the health of older people? Unfortunately, much of the evidence about inequalities in health relates to people of working age. However, in terms of health such a focus is unhelpful, since most morbidity and mortality occurs among people over retirement age. Figure 8.1 shows that in 1991, women aged over 75 accounted for only 9 per cent of the population but experienced 36 per cent of all limiting long-term illness and 68 per cent of all deaths. It is therefore vital not to neglect older people when analysing inequalities in health. For example, women over 75 living in local

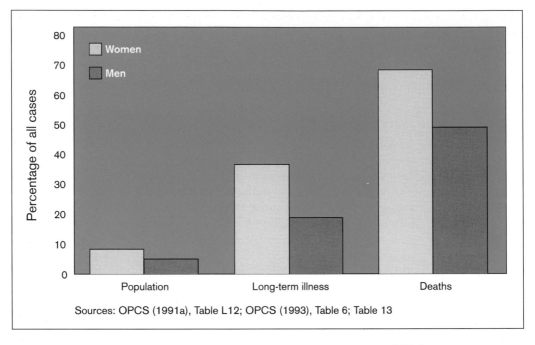

Sources: OPCS (1991a), Table L12; OPCS (1993), Table 6; Table 13

Figure 8.1: Burden of ill health at ages 75 and over, England and Wales, 1991

authority housing and without access to a car have a standardised mortality ratio approximately 20 per cent higher than owner occupiers with a car. For women aged between 60 and 74, the standardised mortality ratio is over 50 per cent higher among the more disadvantaged group (Goldblatt, 1990b). In a multivariate analysis of self-assessed health status, income, car ownership and tenure were all significantly associated with individuals reporting their health as not good after controlling for age and social class. As a result, Arber and Ginn concluded that 'material advantage is critical for an older person's sense of wellbeing' (1993, p. 43).

Disadvantaged circumstances clearly lead to poor health among older people. It is important that more attention is given to designing appropriate policies that promote equity in health among this growing proportion of the population.

Minority ethnic groups

People who classify themselves as belonging to a minority ethnic group have a high probability of experiencing particularly acute forms of disadvantage which exacerbate health inequalities. For example, Oppenheim argues that:

> *black people and other ethnic minority groups are more at risk of high unemployment, low pay, shift work and poor social security rights. Their poverty is caused by ... policies which have often excluded people ... from access to welfare, employment patterns which have marginalised black people and other ethnic minority groups into low-paid manual work, direct and indirect discrimination in social security and the broader experience of racism in society.*

> (1990, p. 91)

One specific illustration of the acute forms of disadvantage facing minority ethnic groups is that, throughout the 1980s, their rates of unemployment were almost double those of white people. To a certain extent such statistics reflect the age and skill structure of the minority ethnic population in Britain. However, even after adjusting for age and educational attainment, minority ethnic groups have higher rates of unemployment than white people, which suggests that discrimination is also a factor (Philpott, 1994).

What do disadvantage and discrimination mean for the health of minority ethnic groups? Unfortunately, illustrating how the considerable disadvantages experienced by minority ethnic groups feed through to poor health is not a simple matter, because most of the research evidence to date has focused on country of birth rather than ethnic identity. Nevertheless, Smaje (1995) highlights a number of recent studies that show raised mortality and morbidity rates among minority ethnic groups compared to the majority white population. Moreover, these indicators of poorer health status cannot be entirely explained by conventional measures of socioeconomic circumstances. Racism and discrimination appear to be implicated as distinct problems that warrant closer attention. For example, Benzeval and colleagues (1992) suggest that experiences of either discrimination at work or racial harassment are associated with poor health status.

The main purpose of this brief summary is to make the plea that what is badly needed in relation not only to ethnic minorities but also to other relatively neglected social groups is a real determination to examine factors that inhibit their prospects of good health, and to identify and promote interventions that will improve their health status. However, the primary objective of this chapter is to focus on the three important policy areas that Ditchley Park participants encouraged us to reconsider. We now turn therefore to a brief review of education, unemployment and childcare.

Education

One important way of tackling inequalities in health would be to improve educational opportunities for the most disadvantaged young people. There is a growing body of evidence that poor socioeconomic circumstances are highly correlated with low levels of educational attainment. In turn, the lack of educational qualifications increases the probability of unemployment and poverty in adulthood, which are associated with poor health outcomes.

Figure 8.2 illustrates the social gradient in educational qualifications. It compares the proportion of workers aged 25–59 in Britain in 1990–91 who either had a degree or no educational qualifications at all by the socioeconomic group of their fathers. One-third of the professional group had a degree compared with 3 per cent of the unskilled manual group. In contrast, almost nine times as many workers with unskilled manual origins have no qualifications compared to those from professional backgrounds. Further evidence of educational inequalities is cited by Edwards and Whitty (1994), who contrast the secondary school examination achievements of male and female pupils at age 16 from professional/managerial groups with those from manual groups. The social gradients are very marked. High examination scores are clearly associated with social advantage for Afro-Caribbean and Asian as well as for white children.

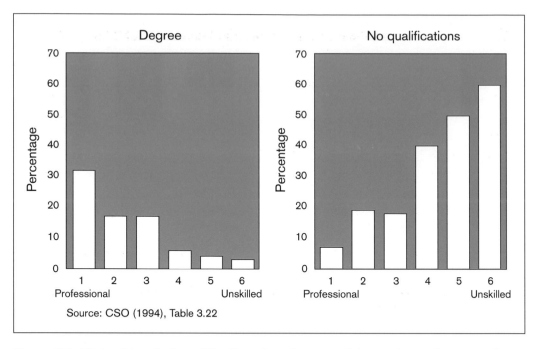

Figure 8.2: Highest level of qualification of workers aged 25–29 by socioeconomic group of father, Great Britain, 1991–92

Low levels of educational attainment are critically important to any understanding of health inequalities because they engender economic insecurity in terms of low earnings and unemployment. Column 1 of Table 8.1 shows that, in 1991, more than 40 per cent of workers without any qualifications were paid less than two-thirds of male median earnings compared with only 6 per cent of those with degrees. Moreover, Schmitt and Wadsworth (1994) have shown that the gap in earning power between the two groups has begun to increase substantially in recent years. Between 1981 and 1991, among full-time male employees aged 20–64, those without qualifications had a modest rise in earnings of 11.3 per cent compared with 27.3 per cent for those with a degree.

Column 2 of Table 8.1 contrasts the experience of workers with a degree with those without qualifications in terms of the proportion of each group who were unemployed in 1992. Men without qualifications were more than three times as likely to be unemployed as those with degrees. The contrasts among people who are in long-term unemployment are even more stark. Column 3 shows that only 4 per cent of individuals in long-term unemployment in 1992 had a degree, whereas 46 per cent lacked any qualifications at all.

Chapter 5 clearly demonstrates that people with low incomes have poorer health status than those who are more affluent. The point we wish to emphasise here is that the lack of educational attainment and opportunities is a key determinant of relative poverty, and that this exacerbates health inequalities. Some commentators would argue that this is irrelevant because educational attainment is entirely a function of an individual's abilities and aspirations, but we reject such assumptions. We believe that many people

Table 8.1: Educational attainment and economic failure in Great Britain in the 1990s

Education	Low pay[1]	Unemployment rate[2]	Long-term unemployment[3]
Degree	5.6	4.4	4.0
No qualifications	42.3	13.7	46.0

Notes:

1 Percentage of male workers with two-thirds or less of male median earnings in 1991. Source: Gregg *et al.* (1994), Table 5.1

2 Percentage of male workers unemployed in 1992. Source: Schmitt and Wadsworth (1994), Table 6.1.3

3 Percentage of people in long-term unemployment with either a degree or no qualifications in 1992. Source: Philpott (1994), Table 6.2.9

have insufficient education and training because of their adverse circumstances. As Edwards and Whitty demonstrate, in our society:

educational opportunities have continued to be more readily available to the socially advantaged to an extent which is unfair and economically unproductive.

(1993, p. 52)

Policy options

It is not our intention to set out a comprehensive agenda for changing educational policies in ways that would maximise opportunities for the most disadvantaged sections of the community. What we can do is highlight two key sets of changes advocated in two recent reports. If these were implemented, their authors believe that they would begin to transform educational opportunities in ways which might have a substantial long-term pay-off in terms of reducing health inequalities.

A better start

The first example of policy innovation is drawn from a report by Sir Christopher Ball, Director of Learning at the Royal Society for the Encouragement of Arts, Manufactures and Commerce, in which he advocates the key principle that 'no child ... should be deprived of opportunity and support for effective early learning' (1994, p. 62). Sir Christopher argues that it is a national scandal that 'the most vulnerable members of society – young children (especially those from deprived or disadvantaged backgrounds)' have been 'deprived of the right start to their lives' (Ball, 1994, p. 7). What is needed is a new approach, one that recognises that preschool education is an essential prerequisite for making the most of formal schooling.

Many children from the most disadvantaged backgrounds, but by no means all, do not attend nursery schools, live in homes without books and other educational materials, and have parents who are not able for one reason or another to provide a stimulating learning environment. Such children are in urgent need of new forms of assistance. At present, when they enter primary schools:

they tend to be bewildered, discouraged and defeated by the challenge of formal learning. They are neither prepared nor ready for it. Such children are likely to become demotivated, drop-outs, or delinquent. They exact a heavy social cost in the longer term.

(Ball, 1994, p. 64)

What is particularly unfortunate about this state of affairs is highlighted by the research evidence that, although all children benefit from high-quality early learning opportunities, 'the effects are strongest in those from disadvantaged backgrounds' (p. 20). Sir Christopher suggests that what is now required is a:

statutory and mandatory responsibility to provide free, high-quality, half-day early learning for all children aged three to four by not later than the year 2000; and that such provision should be adequately resourced and set in an appropriate context of care and support.

(Ball, 1994, p. 62)

There appears to be a political consensus in support of this proposition, but even if preschool facilities cannot be made universally available in the immediate future the needs of the most disadvantaged children should not be ignored. What is now required, therefore, is a real and lasting commitment to making the necessary resources available to deliver change in a way that promotes greater social justice.

Raising standards in deprived areas

Even if action is taken to improve early learning opportunities for future generations of young children, it is also essential to enhance the formal schooling experiences of children who live in the most deprived parts of the country. The need for action in this area was emphasised by the National Commission on Education (NCE, 1993), which advocated – as part of a wide-ranging vision summarised in Box 8.1 – that all citizens should enjoy access to improved educational opportunities as a means to greater economic success and personal satisfaction.

At present, however, educational opportunities are biased in favour of the most advantaged social groups, and those who are able to exploit them obtain substantial economic benefits. There is a growing gap in the modern world between 'knowledge workers' – those who are well educated and trained and can command power and privilege in the marketplace – and the rest of society. There are a diminishing number of jobs for those without qualifications and those that are available are relatively poorly paid. As the Commission points out, 'the threat to social cohesion is obvious' and:

it makes it all the more important and urgent therefore that we should develop educational and training provision suited to the needs and capabilities of the whole population and not only those of the academically more able members of it.

(pp. 37–8)

Box 8.1: The National Commission on Education's vision

1   In all countries **knowledge and applied intelligence** have become central to economic success and personal and social wellbeing.

2   In the United Kingdom much higher achievement in education and training is needed to match world standards.

3   Everyone must want to learn and have ample opportunity and encouragement to do so.

4   All children must achieve a good grasp of literacy and basic skills early on as the foundation for learning throughout life.

5   The full range of people's abilities must be recognised and their development rewarded.

6   High-quality learning depends above all on the knowledge, skill, effort and example of teachers and trainers.

7   It is the role of education **both** to interpret and pass on the values of society **and** to stimulate people to think for themselves and to change the world around them.

Source: NCE (1993), p. xv

Such divisions are only too evident in the most deprived areas of Britain, where multiple disadvantages combine to make educational success difficult to attain. There is now considerable evidence that average levels of educational attainment and participation in post-compulsory education are relatively low in deprived communities compared to more prosperous areas. Barber (1993) cites the judgement of Her Majesty's Inspectorate that 'the poorest schools are those in the inner city taking children from disadvantaged backgrounds' (p. 1). What seems to be essential to improving educational performance in Britain, therefore, is a concerted national policy for improving education in deprived urban areas.

In a background paper for the National Commission, Barber (1993) has outlined a package of fifteen measures which could help to raise educational standards in the poorest areas. The Commission itself particularly emphasised three sets of policy initiatives which would go a long way towards improving the situation in such areas.

- Ensure that resources are allocated in proportion to the more precisely measured educational needs of different areas.

- Give enhanced support to the people who are struggling to provide services in difficult circumstances.

- Develop innovative projects and partnerships to supplement the activities of even the most imaginative and successful schools in disadvantaged areas.

Extra funding for specialist services and a fair distribution of all finance for education may seem an obvious recommendation to make, but the emphasis on retaining and motivating experienced staff is no less important.

It is vital that schools in deprived areas should be able to select and retain teachers and heads who are committed to working in this kind of environment; who believe strongly in the capacity of every pupil to make progress; and whose expectations of pupils are correspondingly high. … Appropriate salary rewards for good teachers in deprived areas are important, but additional measures are needed in order to demonstrate that the skill and professionalism of those who choose to work in disadvantaged areas are valued highly. Professional development is vital as a source of new ideas for dealing with problems as well as a way of renewing commitment and enthusiasm for a demanding task.

(NCE, 1993, p. 178)

Similarly, innovation and enterprise are essential. A wide variety of local organisations must be encouraged to work with schools, and new forms of educational centres must be established so as to motivate those children who find conventional education both daunting and unsatisfying.

Even on the basis of the limited evidence presented here there is little room for doubt that educational opportunities are not equally distributed, and that the adverse consequences are considerable. The lack of educational qualifications greatly increases the risk of poverty-related ill health by exposing people to poor or non-existent employment opportunities. Skills are crucial in a rapidly changing labour market, and those workers without them are seriously disadvantaged. The result is high rates of unemployment, the topic to which we turn next.

Unemployment

For most of the period since 1981 the percentage of the male labour force unemployed and claiming benefit has been above 8.5 per cent – a figure assumed to be a maximum level when the Beveridge plan for social security was formulated in the 1940s. In 1986, and again in 1992 and 1993, the unemployment rate has been above 13 per cent. In July 1993, over three million people were unemployed, and of these, 40 per cent of men and 26 per cent of women had been out of work for over a year – over one million people (Hills, 1993). When the dependants of people who are unemployed are added to the total, sizeable sections of the population are blighted as a direct consequence of unemployment. Moreover, 'the official unemployment rate now seriously understates the extent of joblessness and labour market slack in Britain' (Schmitt and Wadsworth, 1994, p. 114). For example, in 1992 two million men of working age were no longer actively seeking employment over and above the 1.7 million officially unemployed.

The decline in economic activity has been largest among those with the least qualifications. Thirty-three per cent of men without qualifications were without a job in 1992, an increase of 22 per cent since 1977. For those with a degree, only 10 per cent were not in employment, an increase of only 6 per cent over the same period (Schmitt and Wadsworth, 1994). Figure 8.3 shows that unemployment rates are over four times higher among unskilled workers than professional groups (Philpott, 1994).

Unemployment results in considerable financial loss to the people affected. For example, the out-of-work income of a single person or married couple without children is

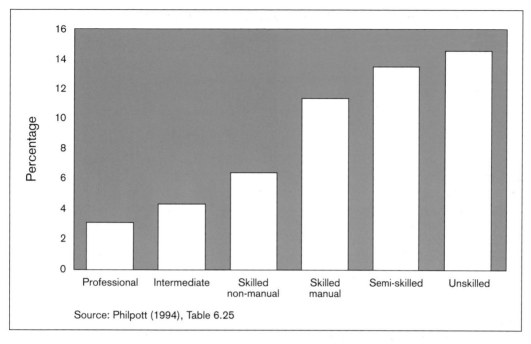

Source: Philpott (1994), Table 6.25

Figure 8.3: Unemployment rates by occupation and skill level, Great Britain, 1992

approximately 48 per cent of income in work. Couples with children receive about 80 per cent of in-work income (Philpott, 1994). Income reductions such as these are a significant cause of poverty. As Benzeval and Webb demonstrate in Chapter 5, almost half of children in families with incomes below 40 per cent of the national average are in two-parent families where neither parent is in full-time work.

Low income is closely associated with poor health. It is hardly surprising, therefore, that there is a strong relationship between unemployment and poor health (Smith, 1987; Bartley, 1994). But the causal links between the two have been much disputed. There is no doubt that unemployment is associated with a variety of measures of ill health. What has been at issue is whether illness results in unemployment or vice versa (see Bartley, 1992). However, the latest evidence suggests that there is both a health selection effect – people with poor health are more likely to be forced out of the labour market - and a direct effect, unemployment itself leads to avoidable morbidity and premature mortality. For example, a recent study based on data from the *British Regional Heart Study* reported that the:

> *increased mortality in men experiencing a loss of employment. ... After adjustment for a wide range of background variables including social class, health behaviour, and health status before loss of employment ... suggests a causal effect.*
>
> (Morris *et al.*, 1994, p. 1139)

This conclusion is based on a prospective study of 6,191 men aged 40–59 who had been continuously employed for at least five years before initial screening in 1978–80. Five years later the employment history and health status of these people were reassessed. Subsequently, any deaths among this group of men were recorded.

The results indicate that those men who reported some interruption to their work experience, either through retirement or unemployment, had almost double the risk of dying, after adjustment for a wide range of confounding factors, than those who remained continuously employed. Not unexpectedly, the greatest risk of early death was found among those men who were not in work because of ill health (odds ratio of 3.14). However, significantly higher relative risks were also identified for men whose experience of unemployment was not obviously related to prior poor health (odds ratio of 1.47). Further evidence from the *Longitudinal Study* shows that men who are unemployed and their wives have raised mortality levels of about 20 per cent, particularly among manual workers (Moser *et al.,* 1990c). The highest SMRs for people who are unemployed are for lung cancer, accidental deaths and suicide.

Unemployment is also associated with higher rates of morbidity (Arber, 1991). For example, studies have consistently found that people who are unemployed have lower levels of psychological wellbeing (Bartley, 1994). They have a higher risk of depression, anxiety, poor self-esteem, neurotic disorders and disturbed sleep. The psychological distress and damage caused by unemployment has been attributed in part to the prevalent attitudes towards unemployed people in our society, and in part to the enforced change in lifestyle brought about by unemployment. People who are unemployed and their families frequently face stigma, humiliation and loss of status, as well as a loss of purpose and structure to their daily life. Some find the loss of a sense of belonging and mattering particularly damaging to mental health. They are also at risk of a decline in physical health if they respond to stress and boredom with increased smoking and a less active lifestyle.

Chronic and persistent unemployment is a major health hazard. The risk of being unemployed is much higher among those with the least education and in unskilled occupations. Unemployment results in poverty, low self-esteem and social isolation. As such it makes a significant contribution to inequalities in health.

Policy options

One of the clearest messages to emerge at Ditchley Park was that no strategy to tackle health inequalities will be worthy of the name if it is not committed to reducing unemployment to the lowest possible level. In recent years a number of organisations have articulated programmes to tackle unemployment including the Social Market Foundation (Skidelsky and Halligan, 1993), *Demos* (Leadbeater and Mulgan, 1994) and the Commission on Social Justice (CSJ) (1994).

For example, in the *Demos* quarterly, Leadbeater and Mulgan highlight 'seven steps to ending unemployment' including making the case:

> *for reforming education to make people employable; for making it easy to create new firms and new jobs; for taxes that stop discrimination against jobs; for rethinking security away from the workplace and towards the individual; for a political commitment to cope with those who nevertheless remain out of work; for new absorptive sectors; and, finally, to bind them all together, for new ethics, based on work and human capital, and linked to common goals and membership in a larger society.*

> (1994, p. 14)

Similarly, the CSJ has developed a job, education and training programme with six clear goals.

- *First, it should create a comprehensive re-employment service.*

- *Second, it should use training investment as a lever to improve people's employability.*

- *Third, it should sponsor 'micro-entrepreneurs' who have the talent to move from unemployment to self-employment.*

- *Fourth, it should offer lone parents additional help with finding good childcare facilities.*

- *Fifth, it should encourage the development of Intermediate Labour Markets – half-way houses to the formal labour market – in areas of greatest economic hardship.*

- *Sixth, it should use wage subsidies to reconnect the registered long-term unemployed to the labour market.*

(1994, p. 172)

Leaving childcare strategies to one side, as these are discussed separately in the next section of this chapter, four common themes can be identified in the proposals developed by Skidelsky and Halligan, *Demos* and the CSJ:

- education and training;

- taxes, benefits and subsidies;

- new patterns of work;

- entrepreneurship.

Education and training

The starting point for many commentators is a belief that success in the international economy of the future will depend to an ever-increasing extent on the intellectual quality of the labour force; access to knowledge and skills will be of paramount importance. Improving economic competitiveness requires a significant increase in national investment in human capital formation in two main ways. First, compulsory schooling should be fundamentally reshaped so as to raise the horizons and standards of the vast majority of children who are middle achievers. Secondly, greater emphasis should be placed on creating a viable and accessible framework for lifetime learning opportunities.

What is particularly important is the provision of new training opportunities for people who are in long-term unemployment. Skidelsky and Halligan (1993) and the CSJ (1994) both argue that current investment in training for people who are unemployed is insufficient, inflexible and irrelevant. The CSJ argues that training should be part of 'a national "learning bank" which enables everybody to have access to lifelong learning' (1994, p. 141). The government, employers and individuals would all contribute to the bank, and resources would be concentrated on improving the educational qualifications of individuals who are unemployed. Skidelsky and Halligan (1993) suggest that people in long-term unemployment should be given training vouchers. More controversially, they argue that unemployment benefits should be linked to attendance at training schemes in the belief that this would counter the loss of self-esteem and apathy which may set in among those out of work for long periods of time.

Taxes, benefits and subsidies

A second strand in any new approach to employment policy must include fiscal initiatives such as:

- creating a more flexible benefit system;

- reorientating the tax system;

- providing wage subsidies.

The benefit system needs to be made more flexible to enable people out of work to undertake training and education without loss of income or to combine part-time or voluntary working with childcare. More radically, the *Demos* report argues that the burden of taxation on employers should be reduced to encourage them to take on more staff. 'The tax system should be overhauled, shifting its bias towards human capital creation' (Leadbeater and Mulgan, 1994, p. 9), by encouraging private investment in education and a progressive reduction in payroll taxes.

Both Skidelsky and Halligan and the CSJ go one step further and argue that employers should be offered subsidies to hire people in long-term unemployment. The CSJ suggests that there are three ways this might be done.

- Employers could be made exempt from paying national insurance for the first year for people they take on who are unemployed.

- People in unemployment could continue to receive benefits for an initial period of employment, providing the employer with free labour, particularly during the initial training period.

- Employers could be given an individual's unemployment benefits for a specified period of time, while they pay the individual a normal wage.

Whatever the specific details of the subsidies are, safeguards will need to be introduced to prevent unscrupulous employers from sacking staff at the end of the subsidy period.

New patterns of work

New ways of working have to be found to achieve sustainable full employment. Leadbeater and Mulgan argue that both national and local government have to be involved with other major institutions in the process of job creation. More specifically, the CSJ suggests there is a need to create what they describe as 'social economy organisations' that would provide employment in projects associated with environmental improvements or energy conservation. People in long-term unemployment would be offered training while in receipt of benefits followed by paid employment on the projects. More radically, Leadbeater and Mulgan argue for the explicit recognition of the existence of 'twin economies'. Alongside the formal world of conventional work they propose, it might be beneficial to provide more positive encouragement for informal cash-in-hand economies.

Much more generally, all participants in the labour market need help to adapt to the changing culture and ethics of work; to recognise that adaptability, teamwork and self-reliance are the qualities that will be needed in the future. The challenge is to find ways of ensuring that the insecurity these changes engender does not become stultifying. Workers will need new forms of support to make the most of their new roles. It may be a banal cliché, but the world of work will have to become a more personal, caring one.

Entrepreneurship

Finally, there is widespread support for the encouragement of a more positive culture of entrepreneurship. This requires financial and other support for people to start new businesses and the removal of some of the most common causes of business failure. For example, Skidelsky and Halligan (1993) suggest that new kinds of agencies to provide loans at low interest rates should be set up to unlock informal venture capital for the establishment of new businesses. More generally, the CSJ advocates a system of support for new business modelled on the Prince's Youth Business Trust, which provides both financial and business support – through mentoring systems – to new concerns. As well as a focus on new start ups, Skidelsky and Halligan (1993) suggest that regulations should be introduced to prevent small businesses going to the wall in economic downturns. This would include legislation to discourage debtors from making late payments and high street banks from levying punitive charges on small businesses, both of which have been the cause of many bankruptcies in the past.

Overview

There are a whole host of other proposals that have been canvassed, some of which are more controversial than others. It has only been possible to touch on a few of them here as the intention of this chapter is primarily to illustrate some of the current policy ideas on each issue, rather than lay out detailed proposals. Nevertheless, the four common themes that we have highlighted do merit closer attention. It is certainly difficult to contest the assertion that it will prove impossible to achieve prosperity and stability without putting policies to tackle unemployment at the top of the political agenda. One of the many measures that would help to transform prospects in this area would be substantial improvements in childcare provision. We consider this issue next.

Childcare provision

The provision of childcare is extremely limited in Britain compared to other European countries (Cohen and Fraser, 1991). A survey of day care services for children under 8, carried out by OPCS in 1991, found that only 8 per cent of preschool children were attending a day nursery, 15 per cent were in nursery education and a further 6 per cent were with a childminder. However, the majority of these children attended the facilities for less than fifteen hours a week. After-school facilities were used by only 18 per cent of children aged 4–7 (DoH, 1994c).

Not only is the provision of childcare very limited, but its costs can be prohibitive for many families with low incomes. One study found that 'more than a half of the independent day nurseries and over three-quarters of all other types of independent institution reported that they had no children from socially disadvantaged homes' (Cohen, 1988, p. 23). Yet local authority provision is restricted and only available to children categorised as 'at risk'. Overall, the inequalities in access to and provision of childcare mean that 'children in poor neighbourhoods are the most likely not to have attended any form of group provision outside of the family before the age of five' (Cohen and Fraser, 1991, p. 121).

Earlier in this chapter we highlighted the benefits for children of preschool education. The additional point to be emphasised here is that the lack of affordable childcare facilities discourages women, particularly those on low incomes, from taking up formal employment and hence exacerbates their own and their family's poverty. For example, a recent policy paper for the Institute for Public Policy Research (IPPR) argued that 'because of its impact on women's earning power and family income, providing childcare is one of the most effective ways of relieving child poverty' (Coote, 1991, p. ii). Such an assertion is supported by a cost-benefit analysis conducted on behalf of the Australian government, which demonstrated the role of public childcare in reducing inequalities in the distribution of family income and providing support against poverty arising from separation, divorce and widowhood (Cohen and Fraser, 1991).

Lack of affordable childcare is particularly damaging for lone parents. As Benzeval and Webb have demonstrated (p. 71), a substantial proportion of families with low incomes are headed by lone parents. For most lone parents income support is the main source of income and accounts for two-thirds of the total (Burghes, 1993). In a Gallup poll for the National Audit Office, three-quarters of lone parents on income support said that the main reason for not working full-time was 'the need to look after children' (NAO, 1991). In another survey of lone parents, a third of respondents stated that the lack of affordable childcare was the main reason for them not working or not working more (Bradshaw and Millar, 1991).

The inability of women in two-parent families to take up employment because of inadequate childcare also increases the risk of family poverty. Cohen and Fraser (1991) analysed Department of Social Security data and found that over one half of two-parent families with both parents working were in the top two income quintiles, compared with 3 per cent of such families in the bottom quintile. For families where only the man worked, four times as many (13 per cent) were in the bottom quintile. This suggests that family poverty could and would be reduced if adequate childcare was provided so that women could participate in formal employment.

The inability of women to participate in employment because of caring responsibilities may harm their health in other ways. Clearly, not all employment is beneficial for women, but in many circumstances paid work may improve their health by providing social contact and support, and by improving their self-esteem and sense of accomplishment as well as providing financial independence (Miles, 1991).

Policy options

The link between low income and poor health is now well established. The provision of childcare is an essential part of any strategy to reduce family poverty. Cohen and Fraser

(1991) have estimated that half of children under 5 living on low incomes could be brought out of poverty if childcare enabled their mothers to work.

In the November 1993 budget, the Chancellor of the Exchequer announced a £40 childcare disregard for families in receipt of family credit, housing benefit and council tax benefit. This allowance was introduced in October 1994, and although it is a welcome initiative it is insufficient. What is urgently needed is a comprehensive government strategy which ensures that affordable, high-quality childcare is available to all families who wish to use it. Cohen and Fraser (1991) suggest that such a strategy should cover a number of different services which are set out in Box 8.2.

Who should provide these services and how they should be financed is a matter for debate. For example, the National Council for One Parent Families (NCOPF, 1994) argues that childcare subsidies should be extended to the tax as well as the benefit system. Such a system would enable all women to benefit from subsidised childcare, but it could be provided by a number of different agencies to suit the family's preferences.

More radically, Cohen and Fraser (1991) argue that childcare should be publicly provided, with parents paying on average 30 per cent of the fees according to their income. Public provision of childcare services, they argue, would:

- provide better access and quality of care by ensuring that workers are appropriately trained and paid;

- deliver the volume of care necessary in a consistent manner;

- be easier to regulate, monitor and evaluate.

Moreover, Cohen and Fraser (1991) argue that the public provision of childcare facilities

---

Box 8.2: Public provision of childcare

Cohen and Fraser argue that publicly provided childcare in Britain should cover:

- day nurseries that combine care and education, provided directly by local authorities or in partnership with a range of other providers;

- a framework of support and regulation for home-based carers including direct employment and links with centre-based care;

- preschool education offering a range of provisions, including family day care and informal services;

- childcare services for school-age children covering both educational and recreational activities, rather than simply being a minding service;

- education authorities should have statutory responsibility for care as well as educational requirements for children aged up to 14 (19 with special needs).

Source: Cohen and Fraser (1991)

---

would actually result in a net gain for the Treasury in terms of reducing the costs of benefits and increasing tax revenues over and above the costs of providing care.

The Commission on Social Justice (1994) also calls for a comprehensive strategy for childcare in Britain. However, it argues that it is not feasible for the government to provide all the facilities. Instead a system of fee relief – combined with user charges – should be introduced for all providers – public, private or voluntary – who meet nationally agreed standards.

How childcare is provided, however, seems less immediately important than ensuring that the quantity and quality of childcare services in Britain are improved, so that it can contribute to an attack on family poverty.

Overview

This final chapter has highlighted some of the key issues that participants at the Ditchley Park seminar felt had been relatively neglected. To begin with, we have argued that the excessive focus on white males of working age, which has dominated the history of health inequalities research in Britain, must give way to a much wider social perspective. In the future, a higher priority should be given to investigating and responding to social inequalities among women, older people and members of minority ethnic groups.

Our second main proposition is related to the belief that any strategy to promote social justice in general and to tackle inequalities in health in particular demands a very wide-ranging and radical reshaping of economic and social policies. In earlier parts of the book a number of contributors have outlined possible new approaches to fairer policies in relation to housing, income maintenance, the NHS and smoking cessation. In this final chapter we also introduce the arguments for a radical reappraisal of education, employment and childcare policies, although the options for change that we highlight are advanced in a more tentative manner than those in the main body of the book.

The policy options we have summarised in this chapter might not be the most appropriate ones, but they are included to remind the reader of the fundamental challenge that provides the *raison d'être* for this book:

> *How can the large and growing social inequalities in health in Britain be substantially reduced?*

We believe the time is long overdue when analysts must go beyond articulating ever more sophisticated statements of the extent of the problem and begin the much more difficult process of advocating policies that will begin to improve the situation. *Tackling Inequalities in Health* represents a modest contribution in that direction, but we recognise that much more detailed work will be required to mobilise public and professional opinion and to engender political will before the prospect of equity in health can be transformed from a distant aspiration into a tangible achievement.

Now is a good time to start.

References

B. Abel-Smith (1986), 'The World Economic Crisis, Part 1: Repercussions on Health', *Health Policy and Planning*, vol. 1, pp. 202–13.

L. Adams (1994), 'Health Promotion in Crisis', *Health Education Journal*, vol. 53, pp. 354–60.

P. Aitken and D. Eadie (1990), 'Reinforcing Effects of Cigarette Advertising on Under-Age Smoking', *British Journal of Addiction*, vol. 85, pp. 399–412.

P. Aitken, D. Leathar and F. O'Hagan (1985), 'Children's Perceptions of Advertisements for Cigarettes', *Social Science and Medicine*, vol. 21, pp. 785–97.

A. Ammerman, B. DeVellis, P. Haines, T. Keyserling, T. Carey, R. DeVellis and R. Simpson (1992), 'Nutrition Education for Cardiovascular Disease Prevention among Low Income Populations – Description and Pilot Evaluation of a Physician-Based Model', *Patient Education and Counseling*, vol. 19, pp. 5–18.

I. Anderson, P. Kemp and D. Quilgars (1993), *Single Homeless People*, HMSO, London.

S. Arber (1991), 'Class, Paid Employment and Family Roles: Making Sense of Structural Disadvantage, Gender and Health Status', *Social Science and Medicine*, vol. 32, no. 4, pp. 425–36.

S. Arber and J. Ginn (1993), 'Gender and Inequalities in Health in Later Life', *Social Science and Medicine: Women, Men and Health*, Special Issue, vol. 36, no. 1, pp. 33–46.

L. Arblaster and M. Hawtin (1993), *Health, Housing and Social Policy*, Socialist Health Association, London.

ASH (Action on Smoking and Health) (1992), *Her Share of Misfortune: Women, Smoking and Low Income, An Expert Report from the ASH Working Group on Women and Smoking*, Action on Smoking and Health and Cancer Research Campaign, London.

ASH (1993), *Tobacco Advertising: The Case for a Ban*, Action on Smoking and Health, London.

A. Atkinson (1994), *Seeking to Explain the Distribution of Income*, Welfare State Programme Discussion Paper 106, Suntory-Toyota International Centre for Economics and Related Disciplines, London School of Economics, London.

A. Atkinson and J. Skegg (Townsend) (1973), 'Anti-Smoking Publicity and the Demand for Tobacco in the UK', *Manchester School*, vol. 41, pp. 265–82.

A. Atkinson and J. Townsend (1977), 'Economic Aspects of Reduced Smoking', *The Lancet*, vol. 2, pp. 492–4.

Audit Commission (1994), *What Seems to be the Matter: Communication Between Hospitals and Patients*, HMSO, London.

A. Babazono and A. Hillman (1994), 'A Comparison of International Health Outcomes and Health Care Spending', *International Journal of Technology Assessment in Health Care*, vol. 10, no. 3, pp. 376–81.

V. Bahl (1990), 'Results of the Asian Mother and Baby Campaign', *Midwife, Health Visitor and Community Nurse*, vol. 23, no. 2, pp. 60–2.

R. Baker (1992), 'General Practice in Gloucestershire, Avon and Somerset: Explaining Variations in Standards', *British Journal of General Practice*, vol. 42, pp. 415–18.

Sir C. Ball (1994), *Start Right: The Importance of Early Learning*, The Royal Society for the Encouragement of Arts, Manufactures and Commerce, London.

M. Barber (1993), *Raising Standards in Deprived Urban Areas*, National Commission on Education Briefing no. 16, Paul Hamlyn Foundation, London.

D. Barker, P. Gluckman, K. Godfrey, J. Harding, J. Owens and J. Robinson (1993), 'Fetal Nutrition and Cardiovascular Disease in Adult Life', *The Lancet,* vol. 341, pp. 938–41.

W. Barker and R. Anderson (1988), *The Child Development Programme: An Evaluation of Process and Outcomes,* Evaluation Document 9, Early Childhood Development Unit, University of Bristol.

T. Baronowski, J. Henske, B. Simons-Morton, J. Palmer, K. Tiernan, P. Hooks and J. Dunn (1990), 'Dietary Change for Cardiovascular Disease Prevention among Black-American Families', *Health Education Research,* vol. 5, pp. 433–43.

A. Barry, R. Carr-Hill and J. Glanville (1991), *Homelessness and Health: What Do We Know? What Should Be Done?,* Discussion Paper 84, Centre for Health Economics, University of York, York.

M. Bartley (1992), *Authorities and Partisans: The Debate on Unemployment and Health,* Edinburgh Education and Society Series, Edinburgh University Press, Edinburgh.

M. Bartley (1994), 'Unemployment and Ill-Health: Understanding the Relationship', *Journal of Epidemiology and Community Health,* vol. 48, pp. 333–7.

R. Beech, G. Bevan and N. Mays (1990), 'Spatial Equity in the NHS: The Death and Re-Birth of RAWP', in A. Harrison and S. Bruscini (eds.), *Health Care UK 1990: An Annual Review of Health Care Policy,* Policy Journals/King's Fund Institute, London, pp. 44–61.

P. Bennett and C. Smith (1992), 'Parents' Attitudes Towards Immunisation in Wales According to Socioeconomic Group: A Preliminary Investigation', *Health Education Journal,* vol. 51, no. 3, pp. 127–31.

Y. Ben-Shlomo and G. Davey Smith (1991), 'Deprivation in Infancy or in Adult Life: Which is More Important for Mortality Risk?', *The Lancet,* vol. 337, pp. 530–4.

Y. Ben-Shlomo and N. Chaturvedi (1994), 'From Surgery to Surgeon: Does Universality of Access Guarantee Equity in Surgical Health Care Provision?', *Journal of Epidemiology and Community Health,* vol. 48, no. 5, p. 504, (abstract).

M. Benzeval and K. Judge (1995), 'Access to Health Care in England: Continuing Inequalities in the Distribution of GPs', (in press).

M. Benzeval, K. Judge and M. Solomon (1992), *The Health Status of Londoners: A Comparative Perspective,* King's Fund London Initiative Working Paper no. 1, King's Fund, London.

M. Benzeval (ed.), D. Blane, K. Judge, M. Marmot, C. Power, M. Whitehead and R. Wilkinson (1994), *Society and Health,* issue 1, King's Fund Institute and Centre for Health and Society, London.

M. Benzeval, K. Judge and C. Smaje (1995), 'Beyond Class, Race and Ethnicity: Deprivation and Health in Britain', *Health Services Research,* Special Issue, vol. 30, no. 1, (in press).

R. Best (1994), 'The Duke of Edinburgh's Inquiry into British Housing: Three Years On', in Wilcox (ed.) (1994a), pp. 7–17.

G. Betts and J. Betts (1990), 'Establishing a Child Health Clinic in a Deprived Area', *Health Visitor,* vol. 63, no. 4, pp. 122–4.

W. Bines (1994), *The Health of Single Homeless People,* Housing Research Finding no. 128, Joseph Rowntree Foundation, York.

C. Blackburn (1991), *Poverty and Health: Working with Families,* Open University Press, Milton Keynes.

C. Blackburn and H. Graham (1992), *Smoking Among Working Class Mothers: Information Pack,* Department of Applied Social Studies, University of Warwick, Coventry.

D. Blane (1985), 'An Assessment of the Black Report's "Explanations of Health Inequalities" ', *Sociology of Health and Illness,* vol. 7, no. 3, pp. 423–45.

D. Blane, G. Davey Smith and M. Bartley (1990), 'Social Class Differences in Years of Potential Life Lost: Size, Trends and Principal Causes', *British Medical Journal,* vol. 301, pp. 429–32.

M. Blaxter (1983), 'Health Services as a Defence Against the Consequences of Poverty in Industrialised Societies', *Social Science and Medicine,* vol. 17, no. 16, pp. 1139–48.

M. Blaxter (1984), 'Equity and Consultation Rates in General Practice', *British Medical Journal*, vol. 288, pp. 1963–7.

M. Blaxter (1989), 'A Comparison of Measures of Inequality in Morbidity', in Fox (ed.) (1989), pp. 199–230.

M. Blaxter (1990), *Health and Lifestyles*, Tavistock/Routledge, London.

BMA (British Medical Association) (1987), *Deprivation and Ill-Health*, British Medical Association Board of Science and Education Discussion Paper, London.

BMA (1994), *Action on Social Inequalities and Health, Proceedings of a European Conference*, Queen Elizabeth Conference Centre, 3–4 May 1994, British Medical Association, the British Medical Journal and the European Public Health Alliance, London.

B. Boardman (1994), 'Energy Efficiency Measures and Social Inequality', in M. Bhatti, J. Brooke and M. Gibson (eds.), *Housing and the Environment: A New Agenda*, Chartered Institute of Housing, London, pp. 107–27.

I. Bowler (1993), ' "They're Not the Same as Us": Midwives' Stereotypes of South Asian Descent Maternity Patients', *Sociology of Health and Illness*, vol. 15, no. 2, pp. 157–78.

S. Boyle and C. Smaje (1993), *Primary Health Care in London: Quantifying the Challenge*, King's Fund London Initiative Working Paper no. 13, King's Fund, London.

J. Bradshaw and J. Millar (1991), *Lone Parent Families in the UK*, Department of Social Security Research Report no. 6, HMSO, London.

J. Bradshaw, L. Hicks and H. Parker (1992), *Summary Budget Standards for Six Households*, Working Paper no. 12, Family Budget Unit, Department of Social Policy, York.

E. Breeze, G. Trevor and A. Wilmot (1991), *General Household Survey 1989*, OPCS Series GHS no. 20, HMSO, London.

Sir J. Brotherston (1976), 'The Galton Lecture, 1975: Inequality, Is it Inevitable?', in C. Carter and J. Peel (eds.), *Equalities and Inequalities in Health, Proceedings of the 12th Annual Symposium of the Eugenics Society*, Academic Press, London, pp. 73–104.

G. Brown and T. Harris (1978), *Social Origins of Depression: A Study of Psychiatric Disorder in Women*, Tavistock, London.

S. Brown and G. Randall (1993), *Permanent Homes for People Living in Short-Life Housing*, Housing Research Findings no. 81, Joseph Rowntree Foundation, York.

I. Buchan and I. Richardson (1973), *Times Study of Consultations in General Practice*, Scottish Health Studies no. 27, Scottish Home and Health Department, Edinburgh.

R. Bunton, R. Burrows, K. Gillen and S. Muncer (1994), *Interventions to Promote Health in Economically Deprived Areas: A Critical Review of the Literature, A Report to the Northern Regional Health Authority*, NHS Executive: Northern and Yorkshire, Newcastle-Upon-Tyne.

L. Burghes (1980), *Living from Hand to Mouth: A Study of 65 Families Living on Supplementary Benefit*, Family Services Unit/Child Poverty Action Group, London.

L. Burghes (1993), *Lone Parents: Policy Options for the 1990s*, Family Policy Studies Centre/Joseph Rowntree Foundation, London/York.

R. Burridge and D. Ormandy (eds.) (1993), *Unhealthy Housing: Research, Remedies and Reform*, E. & F. N. Spon, London.

P. Bush, A. Zackerman, P. Theiss, V. Taggart, C. Horowitz, M. Sheridan and H. Walter (1989), 'Cardiovascular Risk Factor Prevention in Black School Children: Two-Year Results of the "Know Your Body" Program', *American Journal of Epidemiology*, vol. 129, pp. 466–82.

J. Butler, J. Bevan and R. Taylor (1973), *Family Doctors and Public Policy: A Study of Manpower Distribution*, Routledge and Kegan Paul, London.

Cabinet Office (1980), *Review of Government Statistical Services: Report to the Prime Minister by Sir Derek Raynor,* Cabinet Office, London.

CAPT (Child Accident Prevention Trust) (1989), *Basic Principles of Child Accident Prevention,* Child Accident Prevention Trust, London.

J. Carr (1993), *Housing Research News,* vol. 2, no. 1, Office of Housing Research, Fannie Mae, Washington.

R. Carr-Hill and T. Sheldon (1991), 'Designing a Deprivation Payment for General Practitioners: The UPA(8) Wonderland', *British Medical Journal,* vol. 302, pp. 393–6.

R. Carr-Hill and T. Sheldon (1992), 'Rationality and the Use of Formulae in the Allocation of Resources to Health Care', *Journal of Public Health Medicine,* vol. 14, pp. 117–26.

R. Carr-Hill, T. Sheldon, P. Smith, S. Martin, S. Peacock and G. Hardman (1994), 'Allocating Resources to Health Authorities: Development of Method for Small Area Analysis of Use of In-Patient Services', *British Medical Journal,* vol. 309, pp. 1046–9.

V. Carstairs and R. Morris (1991), *Deprivation and Health in Scotland,* Aberdeen University Press, Aberdeen.

A. Cartwright (1970), *Parents and Family Planning Services,* Routledge and Kegan Paul, London.

A. Cartwright and M. O'Brien (1976), 'Social Class Variations in Health Care and in the Nature of General Practitioner Consultations', in M. Stacey (ed.), *The Sociology of the NHS,* Sociological Review Monograph no. 22, University of Keele, Keele, pp. 77–98.

J. Catford, D. Nutbeam and M. Woolaway (1984), 'Effectiveness and Cost Benefits of Smoking Education', *Community Medicine,* vol. 6, pp. 264–72.

I. Chalmers, M. Enkin and M. Keirse (eds.) (1989), *Effective Care in Pregnancy and Childbirth,* vol. 1, Oxford University Press, Oxford.

J. Chetwynd, P. Cooper, R. Brodie and E. Wells (1988), 'Impact of Cigarette Advertising on Aggregate Demand for Cigarettes in New Zealand', *British Journal of Addiction,* vol. 83, pp. 409–14.

P. Cleary, J. Hitchcock and N. Semmers (1986), *Adolescents, Smoking Research and Health Policy,* Institute for the Study of Smoking Behaviour and Policy, Cambridge, Massachusetts.

Cm 555 (1989), *Working for Patients,* HMSO, London.

Cm 849 (1989), *Caring for People: Community Care in the Next Decade and Beyond,* HMSO, London.

Cm 1986 (1992), *The Health of the Nation: A Strategy for Health in England,* HMSO, London.

B. Cohen (1988), *Caring for Children: Services and Policies for Childcare and Equal Opportunities in the United Kingdom, Report for the European Commission's Childcare Network,* Family Policy Studies Centre, London.

B. Cohen (1990), *Caring for Children: The 1990 Report, Report for the European Commission's Childcare Network on Childcare Services and Policy in the UK,* Family Policy Studies Centre, London.

B. Cohen and N. Fraser (1991), *Childcare in a Modern Welfare System: Towards a New National Policy,* Institute for Public Policy and Research, London.

S. Cohen and E. Lichtenstein (1990), 'Perceived Stress, Quitting Smoking, and Smoking Relapse', *Health Psychology,* vol. 9, pp. 466–78.

E. Collins and R. Klein (1980), 'Equity and the NHS: Self-Reported Morbidity, Access, and Primary Care', *British Medical Journal,* vol. 281, pp. 1111–15.

A. Colver, P. Hutchinson and E. Judson (1982), 'Promoting Children's Home Safety', *British Medical Journal,* vol. 285, pp. 1177–80.

Commission on Social Justice (1994), *Social Justice: Strategies for National Renewal, The Report of the Commission on Social Justice,* Vintage, London.

Community Projects Foundation (1988), *Action for Health: Initiatives in Local Communities*, Community Projects Foundation/Health Education Authority/Scottish Health Education Group, London.

P. Constantinides (1988), 'Safe at Home? Children's Accidents and Inequality', *Radical Community Medicine*, Spring, pp. 31–3.

J. Conway (1993), 'Ill-Health and Homelessness: The Effects of Living in Bed-and-Breakfast Accommodation', in Burridge and Ormandy (eds.) (1993), pp. 283–300.

A. Coote (1991), 'Introduction and Summary', in Cohen and Fraser (1991), pp. ii–vi.

A. Coulter (1987), 'Lifestyles and Social Class: Implications for Primary Care', *Journal of the Royal College of General Practitioners*, vol. 37, pp. 533–6.

A. Coulter and A. Baldwin (1987), 'Survey of Population Coverage in Cervical Cancer Screening in the Oxford Region', *Journal of the Royal College of General Practitioners*, vol. 37, pp. 441–3.

A. Cox, A. Pound, M. Mills, C. Puckering and A. Owen (1991), 'Evaluation of a Home Visiting and Befriending Scheme for Young Mothers: Newpin', *Journal of the Royal Society of Medicine*, vol. 84, pp. 217–20.

B. Cox (1987), 'Blood Pressure and Respiratory Function', in Cox *et al.* (1987), pp. 17–33.

B. Cox, M. Blaxter, A. Buckle, N. Fenner, J. Golding, M. Gore, F. Huppert, J. Nickson, M. Roth, J. Stark, M. Wadsworth and M. Whichelow (1987), *The Health and Lifestyle Survey: Preliminary Report of a Nationwide Survey of the Physical and Mental Health, Attitudes and Lifestyle of a Random Sample of 9,003 British Adults*, Health Promotion Research Trust, London.

I. Crawford, S. Smith and S. Webb (1993), *VAT on Domestic Energy*, IFS Commentary no. 39, Institute for Fiscal Studies, London.

P. Croft and A. Rigby (1994), 'Socioeconomic Influences on Back Problems in the Community in Britain', *Journal of Epidemiology and Community Health*, vol. 48, pp. 166–70.

CSO (Central Statistical Office) (1991), *Family Spending: A Report on the 1990 Family Expenditure Survey*, HMSO, London.

CSO (1993), *Family Spending: A Report on the 1992 Family Expenditure Survey*, HMSO, London.

CSO (1994), *Social Trends 24, 1994 Edition*, HMSO, London.

R. Cummins, B. Jarman and P. White (1981), 'Do General Practitioners have Different "Referral Thresholds"?', *British Medical Journal*, vol. 282, pp. 1037–9.

E. Dahl (1993), 'Social Inequality in Health – The Role of the Healthy Worker Effect', *Social Science and Medicine*, vol. 36, no. 8, pp. 1077–88.

G. Dahlgren (1993), 'Economic Analysis of Health Development', *Newsletter on Health Care in Developing Countries: Health Economics*, vol. 2, pp. 4–7.

G. Dahlgren and F. Diderichsen (1986), 'Strategies for Equity in Health: Report from Sweden', *International Journal of Health Services*, vol. 16, pp. 517–37.

G. Dahlgren and M. Whitehead (1991), *Policies and Strategies to Promote Social Equity in Health*, Institute for Futures Studies, Stockholm (Mimeo).

G. Dahlgren and M. Whitehead (1992), *Policies and Strategies to Promote Equity in Health*, World Health Organization, Copenhagen.

G. Davey Smith, D. Blane and M. Bartley (1994), 'Explanations for Socioeconomic Differentials in Mortality: Evidence from Britain and Elsewhere', *European Journal of Public Health*, vol. 4, no. 2, pp. 131–44.

J. Davies and M. Kelly (eds.) (1993), *Healthy Cities: Research and Practice*, Routledge, London.

DE (Department of Employment) (1962), *Family Expenditure Survey 1961*, HMSO, London.

DE (1976), *Family Expenditure Survey 1975*, HMSO, London..

DE (1981), *Family Expenditure Survey 1980*, HMSO, London.

DE (1987), *Family Expenditure Survey 1986*, HMSO, London.

DE (Department of the Environment) (1993), *English House Condition Survey 1991*, HMSO, London.

T. Delamothe (1991), 'Social Inequalities in Health', *British Medical Journal*, vol. 303, pp. 1046–50.

G. Desplanques (1984), *La Mortalité des Adults: Résultats de 2 Etudes Longitudinales (période 1955–80)*, INSEE, Paris, quoted in Kunst and Mackenbach (1994), p. 31.

DHSS (Department of Health and Social Security) (1976), *Sharing Resources for Health in England: Report of the Resource Allocation Working Party*, HMSO, London.

DHSS (1988), *Review of the Resource Allocation Working Party Formula: Final Report by the NHS Management Board*, DHSS, London.

DHSSNI (Department of Health and Social Services, Northern Ireland) (1992), *A Regional Strategy for Northern Ireland 1992–97*, Department of Health and Social Services, Belfast.

F. Diderichsen (1990), 'Health and Social Inequities in Sweden', in Illsley and Svensson (eds.) (1990), pp. 359–67.

J. Dixon, M. Dinwoodie, D. Hodson, S. Dodd, T. Poltorak, C. Garrett, P. Rice, I. Doncaster and M. Williams (1994), 'Distribution of NHS Funds Between Fundholding and Non-Fundholding Practices', *British Medical Journal*, vol. 309, pp. 30–4.

DoH (Department of Health) (1991), *On the State of the Public Health for the Year 1990*, HMSO, London.

DoH (1992), *Effect of Tobacco Advertising on Tobacco Consumption: A Discussion Document Reviewing the Evidence*, Economics and Operational Research Division, Department of Health, London.

DoH (1993), *Health Service Indicators Dataset*, Department of Health, London.

DoH (1994a), *Smoke Free for Health: An Action Plan to Achieve the Health of the Nation Targets on Smoking*, Department of Health, HMSO, London.

DoH (1994b), *On the State of the Public Health: The Annual Report of the Chief Medical Officer of the Department of Health for the Year 1993*, HMSO, London.

DoH (1994c), *OPCS Survey of Day Care Services for Children: Summary of the Report*, Department of Health, London.

R. Doll (1992), 'Health and the Environment in the 1990s', *American Journal of Public Health*, vol. 82, pp. 933–41.

N. Drummond (1989), 'Evaluation of a Community Health Project: The Experience from West Granton, Edinburgh', in Martin and McQueen (eds.) (1989), pp. 311–15.

DSS (Department of Social Security) (1993), *Households Below Average Income 1979 – 1990/91: A Statistical Analysis*, Government Statistical Service, HMSO, London.

DSS (1994a), *Households Below Average Income 1979 – 1991/92: A Statistical Analysis*, Government Statistical Service, HMSO, London.

DSS (1994b), *The Take-Up of Income-Related Benefits 1991*, Analytical Services Department, DSS, London.

DTI (Department of Trade and Industry) (1991), *Home and Leisure Accident Research: Twelfth Annual Report, 1988 Data*, DTI Consumer Safety Unit, London.

B. Durston and K. Jamrozik (eds.) (1990), *Proceedings of the Seventh World Conference on Tobacco and Health*, Organising Committee of Seventh World Conference on Tobacco and Health, Perth, Australia.

M. Eames, Y. Ben-Shlomo and M. Marmot (1993), 'Social Deprivation and Premature Mortality: Regional Comparisons Across England', *British Medical Journal*, vol. 307, pp. 1097–102.

T. Eardley (1989), *Move-On Housing*, Single Homeless in London/National Federation of Housing Associations, London.

T. Edwards and G. Whitty (1994), 'Education: Opportunity, Equality and Efficiency', in Glyn and Miliband (eds.) (1994), pp. 44–64.

G. Egger, W. Fitzgerald, G. Frape, A. Manaem, P. Robinstein, C. Tyler and B. McKay (1983), 'Results of Large Scale Media Anti-Smoking Campaign in Australia: North Coast "Quit for Life" Programme', *British Medical Journal,* vol. 287, pp. 1125–8.

EL(94)79, *Developing NHS Purchasing and GP Fundholding,* letter from Director of Planning and Performance Management, NHS Executive, Leeds.

D. Elbourne, A. Oakley and I. Chalmers (1989), 'Social and Psychological Support During Pregnancy', in Chalmers *et al.* (eds.) (1989), pp. 221–36.

A. Elder, T. Shaw, C. Turnbull and I. Starkey (1991), 'Elderly and Younger Patients Selected to Undergo Coronary Angiography', *British Medical Journal,* vol. 303, pp. 950–3.

J. Ellis (1989), *Breaking New Ground: Community Development in Asian Communities,* Bedford Square Press of the National Council for Voluntary Organisations, Community Projects Foundation, London.

H. Elmén (1993), 'Infant Mortality: Social Inequality in a Swedish City', *European Journal of Public Health,* vol. 3, no. 4, pp. 237–41.

J. Ermisch (1990), *Fewer Babies, Longer Lives: Policy Implications of Current Demographic Trends,* Joseph Rowntree Foundation, York.

S. Esrey, J. Potash, L. Roberts and C. Shiff (1990), *Health Benefits from Improvements in Water Supply and Sanitation: Survey and Analysis of the Literature on Selected Diseases,* WASH Technical Report no. 66, US Agency for International Development, Washington DC.

M. Evans, D. Piachaud and H. Sutherland (1994), *The Effect of the 1986 Social Security Act on Family Incomes,* Social Policy Research Finding no. 54, Joseph Rowntree Foundation, York.

Faculty of Public Health Medicine (1991), *UK Levels of Health,* Faculty of Public Health Medicine, London.

W. Farr (1860), 'On the Construction of Life Tables, Illustrated by a New Life Table of the Healthy Districts of England', *Journal of Institute of Actuaries,* IX.

FDL(94)68, *Revenue Allocations 1995/96,* letter from Director of Finance and Corporate Information, NHS Executive, Leeds.

G. Forwell (1992), *The Annual Report of the Director of Public Health,* Greater Glasgow Health Board, Glasgow.

J. Fox (ed.) (1989), *Health Inequalities in European Countries,* European Science Foundation, Gower, Aldershot.

J. Fox, P. Goldblatt and D. Jones (1990), 'Social Class Mortality Differentials: Artefact, Selection or Life Circumstances', in Goldblatt (ed.) (1990a), pp. 100–9.

H. Freeman (1993), 'Mental Health and High-Rise Housing', in Burridge and Ormandy (eds.) (1993), pp. 168–90.

K. French, A. Porter, S. Robinson, F. McCallum, J. Howie and M. Roberts (1982), 'Attendance at a Breast Screening Clinic: A Problem of Administration or Attitudes?', *British Medical Journal,* vol. 285, pp. 617–20.

J. Gabe and P. Williams (1993), 'Women, Crowding and Mental Health', in Burridge and Ormandy (eds.) (1993), pp. 191–208.

C. Gale (1994), *Anti-Poverty Strategy and Actions,* Nottingham City Council, Nottingham

A. Gepkens and L. Gunning-Schepers (1993), *Interventions for Addressing Socioeconomic Inequalities in Health,* Institute of Social Medicine, University of Amsterdam (in Dutch).

T. Gibson (1993), *Meadowell Community Development,* Neighbourhood Initiatives Foundation, Telford.

S. Gillam (1992), 'Provision of Health Promotion Clinics in Relation to Population Need: Another Example of the Inverse Care Law', *British Journal of General Practice*, vol. 42, pp. 54–6.

P. Ginnety, J. Wilde and M. Black (1989), 'Participation in Practice: An Example from Belfast', in Martin and McQueen (eds.) (1989), pp. 289–96.

C. Glendinning and J. Millar (eds.) (1992), *Women and Poverty in Britain: The 1990s,* Harvester Wheatsheaf, Hemel Hempstead.

A. Glyn and D. Miliband (eds.) (1994), *Paying for Inequality: The Economic Cost of Social Injustice,* Rivers Oram Press, London.

T. Glynn (1989), 'Essential Elements of School Based Smoking Prevention Programmes', *Journal of School Health*, vol. 59, pp. 181–8.

C. Godfrey and A. Maynard (1988), 'Economic Aspects of Tobacco Use and Taxation Policy', *British Medical Journal*, vol. 297, pp. 339–43.

P. Goldblatt (ed.) (1990a), *Longitudinal Study: Mortality and Social Organisation 1971–1981,* OPCS series LS no. 6, HMSO, London.

P. Goldblatt (1990b), 'Mortality and Alternative Social Classifications', in Goldblatt (ed.) (1990a), pp. 164–92.

A. Goodman and S. Webb (1994), *For Richer for Poorer: The Changing Distribution of Income in the UK, 1961–1991,* IFS Commentary no. 42, Institute for Fiscal Studies, London.

H. Graham (1984), *Women, Health and the Family,* Wheatsheaf Books Ltd., Brighton.

H. Graham (1986), *Caring for the Family,* Research Report no. 1, Health Education Council, London.

H. Graham (1987), 'Women's Smoking and Family Health', *Social Science and Medicine*, vol. 25, no. 1, pp. 47–56.

H. Graham (1993a), *Hardship and Health in Women's Lives,* Harvester/Wheatsheaf, Hemel Hempstead.

H. Graham (1993b), *When Life's a Drag: Women, Smoking and Disadvantage,* Department of Health, HMSO, London.

P. Gregg, S. Machin and A. Manning (1994), 'High Pay, Low Pay and Labour Market Efficiency' in Glyn and Miliband (eds.) (1994), pp. 100–13.

J. Gregory, K. Foster, H. Tyler and M. Wiseman (1990), *The Dietary and Nutritional Survey of British Adults: A Survey Carried Out by the Social Survey Division of OPCS with Dietary and Nutritional Evaluations by the Ministry of Agriculture, Fisheries and Food and the Department of Health,* HMSO, London.

J. Griffiths, R. Pollock, D. Grice, J. Glasson and R. Dunkley (1991), 'Lessons in Class', *Health Service Journal*, 22 August, pp. 20–1.

M. Haan, G. Kaplan and T. Camacho (1987), 'Poverty and Health: Prospective Evidence from the Alameda County Study', *American Journal of Epidemiology*, vol. 125, no. 6, pp. 989–98.

A. Hacker (1992), *Two Nations: Black and White, Separate, Hostile, Unequal,* Ballantine, New York.

J. Hamilton (1972), 'The Demand for Cigarettes: Advertising, the Health Scare and the Cigarette Advertising Ban', *Review of Economic Statistics*, vol. 54, pp. 401–10.

R. Hancock and P. Weir (1994), *The Financial Well-Being of Elderly People,* Social Policy Research Finding no. 57, Joseph Rowntree Foundation, York.

R. Harrison and J. Chetwynd (1990), 'The Impact of Cigarette Advertising on Aggregate Demand for Cigarettes in New Zealand', in Durston and Jamrozik (eds.) (1990), pp. 768–74.

N. Hart (1986), 'Inequalities in Health: The Individual Versus the Environment', *Journal of Royal Statistical Society (series A)*, vol. 149, part 3, pp. 228–46.

R. Hartley, J. Charlton, C. Harris and B. Jarman (1984), 'Influence of Patient Characteristics on Test Ordering in General Practice', *British Medical Journal*, vol. 289, pp. 735–8.

J. Hasan (1989), 'Way-of-Life, Stress and Differences in Morbidity Between Occupational Classes', in Fox (ed.) (1989), pp. 372–85.

B. Haylock (ed.) (1993), *Responding to the Challenge of Fuel Poverty,* Report of Joseph Rowntree Foundation Seminar, September 1992, Joseph Rowntree Foundation, York.

R. Haynes (1991), 'Inequalities in Health and Health Service Use: Evidence from the General Household Survey', *Social Science and Medicine,* vol. 33, no. 4, pp. 361–8.

HC Debates (1993), *Weekly Hansard: Written Answers,* 27 July, col. 1010.

HEA (Health Education Authority) (1989), *Diet, Nutrition and 'Healthy Eating' in Low Income Groups,* Health Education Authority, London.

HEA (1991), *Smoking, Health Update no. 2,* Health Education Authority, London.

Health Promotion Authority for Wales (1990), *Health for All in Wales: Health Promotion Challenges for the 1990s, Part B,* Health Promotion Authority for Wales, Cardiff.

U. Helmert and S. Shea (1994), 'Social Inequalities and Health Status in Western Germany', *Public Health,* vol. 108, pp. 341–56.

C. Hicks and L. Hayes (1991), 'Linkworkers in Antenatal Care: Facilitators of Equal Opportunities in Health Provision or Salves for the Management of Conscience?', *Health Services Management Research,* vol. 4, no. 2, pp. 89–93.

J. Hills (1993), *The Future of Welfare: A Guide to the Debate,* Joseph Rowntree Foundation, York.

R. Hobbs (1993), 'Deprivation Payments: Still Awaiting Change', *British Medical Journal,* vol. 306, pp. 534–5.

J. Holden, R. Sagovsky and J. Cox (1989), 'Counselling in a General Practice Setting: Controlled Study of Health Visitor Intervention in Treatment of Postnatal Depression', *British Medical Journal,* vol. 298, pp. 223–6.

House of Lords (1991), 'Oral Evidence by the Royal Institute of British Architects', in House of Lords European Community Sub-Committee B: Energy, Industry and Transport, *Energy and the Environment,* 13th Report, Session 1990–91, HMSO, London.

M. Howard (1993), 'The Effects on Human Health of Pest Infestation in Houses', in Burridge and Ormandy (eds.) (1993), pp. 256–82.

S. Hunt (1989), *Community Development and Health Promotion in a Deprived Area: Final Report,* Working Paper, Research Unit in Health and Behavioural Change, Edinburgh.

S. Hunt (1990), 'Emotional Distress and Bad Housing', *Health and Hygiene,* vol. 11, pp. 72–9.

S. Hunt (1993), 'The Relationship Between Research and Policy: Translating Knowledge into Action', in Davies and Kelly (eds.) (1993), pp. 71–82.

J. Hurst (1985), *Financing Health Services in the United States, Canada and Britain,* Nuffield/Leverhulme Fellowship Report, King Edward's Hospital Fund for London, London.

S. Huttly (1990), 'The Impact of Inadequate Sanitary Conditions on Health in Developing Countries', *World Health Statistics Quarterly,* vol. 43, pp. 118–26.

R. Illsley (1955), 'Social Class Selection and Class Differences in Relation to Still Births and Infant Deaths', *British Medical Journal,* ii, pp. 1520–4.

R. Illsley (1986), 'Occupational Class, Selection and the Production of Inequalities in Health', *The Quarterly Journal of Social Affairs,* vol. 2, no. 2, pp. 151–65.

R. Illsley and P-G. Svensson (eds.) (1990), *Social Science and Medicine: Health Inequities in Europe,* Special Issue, vol. 31, no. 3, pp. 223–420.

ILO (International Labour Office) (ed.) (1992), *Preventing Stress at Work: Conditions of Work Digest,* vol. 11, number 2, International Labour Office, Geneva.

Independent Scientific Committee on Smoking and Health (1988), *Fourth Report of the Independent Scientific Committee on Smoking and Health, Chaired by Sir Peter Froggatt*, HMSO, London.

B. Ineichen (1993), *Homes and Health: How Housing and Health Interact*, E. & F. N. Spon, London.

Insée Comptes Nationaux (1990), 'Dominique Darman', *INSEE Premiere*, no. 100, Paris.

B. Jacobson, A. Smith and M. Whitehead (eds.) (1991), *The Nation's Health: A Strategy for the 1990s*, King Edward's Hospital Fund for London, London.

J. James, P. Lawson, P. Male and A. Oakhill (1989), 'Preventing Iron Deficiency in Pre-School Children by Implementing an Educational and Screening Programme in an Inner City Practice', *British Medical Journal*, vol. 299, pp. 838–40.

K. Jamrozik, M. Vessey, G. Fowler, N. Wald, G. Parker and H. van Vunakis (1984), 'Controlled Trials of Three Different Anti-Smoking Interventions in General Practice', *British Medical Journal*, vol. 288, pp. 1499–503.

J. Johnson (1975), unpublished paper summarised in *Tobacco*, London.

P. Johnson and S. Webb (1993), 'Explaining the Growth in UK Income Inequality 1979–1988', *Economic Journal Conference Papers*, vol. 103, no. 417, pp. 429–35.

Z. Johnson, F. Howell and B. Molloy (1993), 'Community Mothers Programme: Randomised Controlled Trial of Non-Professional Intervention in Parenting', *British Medical Journal*, vol. 306, pp. 1449–52.

Joseph Rowntree Foundation (1991), *Inquiry into British Housing, Second Report June 1991, Chaired by HRH The Duke of Edinburgh KG KT*, Joseph Rowntree Foundation, York.

Joseph Rowntree Foundation (1995), *Inquiry into Income and Wealth, Chaired by Sir Peter Barclay*, vol. 1. Joseph Rowntree Foundation, York.

K. Judge and M. Benzeval (1993), 'Health Inequalities: New Concerns about the Children of Single Mothers', *British Medical Journal*, vol. 306, pp. 677–80.

K. Judge and N. Mays (1994a), 'Allocating Resources for Health and Social Care in England', *British Medical Journal*, vol. 308, pp. 1363–6.

K. Judge and N. Mays (1994b), 'A New Approach to Weighted Capitation', *British Medical Journal*, vol. 309, pp. 1031–2.

R. Karasek (1992), 'Stress Prevention Through Work Re-Organisation: A Summary of 19 Case Studies', in ILO (ed.) (1992), pp, 23–41.

R. Karasek and T. Theorell (1990), *Healthy Work: Stress, Productivity and the Reconstruction of Working Life*, Basic Books, New York.

J. Kasarda (1993), *Inner City Concentrated Poverty in Neighbourhood Distress, 1970–1990*, University of North Carolina, USA.

F. Kee, B. Gaffney, S. Currie and D. O'Reilly (1993), 'Access to Coronary Catheterisation: Fair Shares for All?', *British Medical Journal*, vol. 307, pp. 1305–7.

M. Kelly, J. Davies and B. Charlton (1993), 'Healthy Cities: A Modern Problem or a Post-Modern Solution?', in Davies and Kelly (eds.) (1993), pp. 159–67.

N. Kistin, D. Benton, S. Rao and M. Sullivan (1990), 'Breast-Feeding Rates among Black Urban Low-Income Women: Effect of Prenatal Education', *Pediatrics*, vol. 86, pp. 741–6.

E. Kitagawa and P. Hauser (1973), *Differential Mortality in the United States: A Study in Socioeconomic Epidemiology*, Harvard University Press, Cambridge, Massachusetts.

M. Kogevinas (1990), *Longitudinal Study: Socio-Demographic Differences in Cancer Survivors 1971–1983*, OPCS series LS no. 5, HMSO, London.

M. Kogevinas, M. Marmot, J. Fox and P. Goldblatt (1991), 'Socioeconomic Differences in Cancer Survival', *Journal of Epidemiology and Community Health*, vol. 45, pp. 216–19.

A. Kunst and J. Mackenbach (1994), *Measuring Socioeconomic Inequalities in Health*, World Health Organization Regional Office for Europe, Copenhagen.

Z. Kurtz, R. Thornes and S. Wolkind (1994), *Services for the Mental Health of Children and Young People in England: A National Review*, Maudsley Hospital and South Thames (West) Regional Health Authority, London.

D. Lader and J. Matheson (1991), *Smoking Among Secondary School Children in England 1990: An Enquiry Carried Out by Social Survey Division of OPCS*, HMSO, London.

R. Lagasse, P. Humblet, A. Lenaerts, I. Godin and G. Moens (1990), 'Health and Social Inequities in Belgium', in Illsley and Svensson (eds.) (1990), pp. 237–48.

D. Laidlaw, P. Bloom, A. Hughes, J. Sparrow and V. Marmion (1994), 'The Sight Test Fee: Effect on Ophthalmology Referrals and Rate of Glaucoma Detection', *British Medical Journal*, vol. 309, pp. 634–6.

C. Lambert, S. Jeffers, P. Burton and G. Bramley (1992), *Homelessness in Rural Areas*, Rural Development Commission, London.

T. Lang, C. Andrews, C. Bedale, E. Hannon and J. Hulme (1984), *Jam Tomorrow?*, Food Policy Unit, Manchester Polytechnic, Manchester.

M. Laugesen and C. Meads (1990), 'Tobacco Advertising Restrictions and Consumption in OECD Countries 1960–86', in Durston and Jamrozik (eds.) (1990), pp. 126–9.

I. Lazar, R. Darlington, H. Murray, J. Royce and A. Snipper (1982), 'Lasting Effects of Early Education: A Report from the Consortium of Longitudinal Studies', *Monograph of the Society for Research in Child Development*, serial no. 195, vol. 47, no. 195, nos. 2–3.

C. Leadbeater and G. Mulgan (1994), 'The End of Unemployment: Bringing Work to Life', *Demos*, issue 2, pp. 4–14.

P. Leather and S. Mackintosh (1994), *Renovation Grants and the Condition of Older Housing*, Housing Research Findings no. 104, Joseph Rowntree Foundation, York.

S. Leather (1992), 'Less Money, Less Choice: Poverty and Diet in the UK Today', in National Consumer Council (ed.), *Your Food: Whose Choice?*, HMSO, London, pp. 72–94.

F. Ledwith (1984), 'Does Tobacco Sports Sponsorship on Television Act as Advertising to Children?', *Health Education Journal*, vol. 43, pp. 85–8.

J. Le Grand (1978), 'The Distribution of Public Expenditure: The Case of Health Care', *Economica*, vol. 45, pp. 125–42.

P. Lehmann, C. Mamboury and C. Minder (1990), 'Health and Social Inequities in Switzerland', in Illsley and Svensson (eds.) (1990), pp. 369–86.

D. Leon (1988), *Longitudinal Study: Social Distribution of Cancer*, OPCS series LS no. 3, HMSO, London.

D. Leon, D. Vågerö and P. Otterblad Olausson (1992), 'Social Class Differences in Infant Mortality in Sweden: A Comparison with England and Wales', *British Medical Journal*, vol. 305, pp. 687–91.

L. Levi (1992), 'Managing Stress in Work Settings at the National Level in Sweden', in ILO (ed.) (1992), pp. 139–43.

J. Lewis and D. Piachaud (1992), 'Women and Poverty in the Twentieth Century', in Glendinning and Millar (eds.) (1992), pp. 27–45.

E. Lewit and D. Coate (1982), 'The Potential for Using Excise Taxes to Reduce Smoking', *Journal of Health Economics*, vol. 1, pp. 121–45.

E. Lewit, D. Coate and M. Grossman (1981), 'The Effects of Government Regulations on Teenage Smoking', *Journal of Law and Economics*, vol. 14, pp. 545–69.

C. Liberato, B. Eriacho, J. Schmiering and M. Krump (1989), 'Safesmart Safety Seat Intervention Project: A Successful Program for the Medically-Indigent', *Patient Education and Counseling*, vol. 13, pp. 161–70.

K. Lloyd (1993), 'Mothering Instinct', *Nursing Times*, vol. 89, no. 26, pp. 42–4.

D. Logie and J. Woodroffe (1993), 'Structural Adjustment: The Wrong Prescription for Africa', *British Medical Journal*, vol. 307, pp. 41–4.

S. Lowry (1990), 'Getting Things Done', *British Medical Journal*, vol. 300, pp. 390–2.

J. Lumley and J. Astbury (1989), 'Advice for Pregnancy', in Chalmers *et al.* (eds.) (1989), pp. 241–54.

B. Lundberg (1991), *The LO Health Project: Trade Union Health Promotion in Sweden*, paper presented to the European Conference on Health Promotion in the Workplace, April, Barcelona.

O. Lundberg and J. Fritzell (1994), 'Income Distribution, Income Change and Health: On the Importance of Absolute and Relative Income for Health Status in Sweden', in WHO (ed.), *Economic Change, Social Welfare and Health in Europe*, European Series no. 54, WHO Publications, Copenhagen, pp. 37–58.

M. Lynch (1994), 'Do Deprivation Supplements Compensate GPs for Extra Workload or for Low Uptake of Services?', *Journal of Epidemiology and Community Health*, vol. 48, no. 5, p. 496, (abstract).

S. Macintyre (1986), 'The Patterning of Health by Social Position in Contemporary Britain: Directions for Sociological Research', *Social Science and Medicine*, vol. 23, no. 4, pp. 393–415.

S. Macintyre (1989), 'The Role of Health Services in Relation to Inequalities in Health in Europe', in Fox (ed.) (1989), pp. 317–32.

J. Mackenbach (1993), 'Inequalities in Health in The Netherlands According to Age, Gender, Marital Status, Level of Education, Degree of Organisation, and Region', *European Journal of Public Health*, vol. 3, no. 2, pp. 112–18.

J. Mackenbach (1994), 'Socioeconomic Inequalities in Health in The Netherlands: Impact of a Five-Year Research Programme', *British Medical Journal*, vol. 309, pp. 1487–91.

G. Macquart-Moulin, G. Fancello, A. Vincent, C. Julian, C. Baret and S. Ayme (1990), 'Évaluation des Effets d'une Campagne de Soutien à L'allaitement Exclusif au Sein à un Mois', *Revue Epidémiologique et Santé Publique*, vol. 38, pp. 201–90.

A. Majeed and A. Pollock (1993), 'Health Authorities Should Monitor Equity of Service', *British Medical Journal*, vol. 306, p. 1689, (letter).

A. Majeed, D. Cook, H. Anderson, S. Hilton, S. Bunn and C. Stones (1994a), 'Using Patient and General Practice Characteristics to Explain Variations in Cervical Smear Uptake Rates', *British Medical Journal*, vol. 308, pp. 1272–6.

F. Majeed, N. Chaturvedi, R. Reading and Y. Ben-Shlomo (1994b), 'Monitoring and Promoting Equity in Primary and Secondary Care', *British Medical Journal*, vol. 308, pp. 1426–9.

T. Markus (1993), 'Cold, Condensation and Housing Poverty', in Burridge and Ormandy (eds.) (1993), pp. 141–67.

M. Marmot and T. Theorell (1988), 'Social Class and Cardiovascular Disease: The Contribution of Work', *International Journal of Health Services*, vol. 18, no. 4, pp. 659–74.

M. Marmot, M. Shipley and G. Rose (1984), Inequalities in Death – Specific Explanations of a General Pattern?', *The Lancet*, May 5, pp. 1003–6.

A. Marsh and J. Matheson (1983), *Smoking Attitudes and Behaviour*, HMSO, London.

A. Marsh and S. McKay (1994), *Poor Smokers*, Policy Studies Institute, London.

G. Marsh and D. Channing (1987), 'Comparison in Use of Health Services Between a Deprived and an Endowed Community', *Archives of Diseases in Childhood*, vol. 62, pp. 392–6.

G. Marsh and D. Channing (1988), 'Narrowing the Health Gap Between a Deprived and an Endowed Community', *British Medical Journal*, vol. 296, pp. 173–6.

T. Martelin (1994), 'Mortality by Indicators of Socioeconomic Status Amongst the Finnish Elderly', *Social Science and Medicine*, vol. 38, no. 9, pp. 1257–78.

C. Martin, S. Platt and S. Hunt (1987), 'Housing Conditions and Ill-Health', *British Medical Journal*, vol. 294, pp. 1125–7.

C. Martin and D. McQueen (eds.) (1989), *Readings for a New Public Health*, Edinburgh University Press, Edinburgh.

P. Matthews (1986), 'Medicine and the Media', *British Medical Journal*, vol. 293, p. 442.

J. Mayer, B. Hawkins and R. Todd (1990), 'A Randomised Evaluation of Smoking Cessation Interventions for Pregnant Women at a WIC Clinic', *American Journal of Public Health*, vol. 80, pp. 76–8.

N. Mays (1989), 'NHS Resource Allocation after the 1989 White Paper: A Critique of the Research for the RAWP Review', *Community Medicine*, vol. 11, pp. 173–86.

B. McAvoy and R. Raza (1988), 'Asian Women: (i) Contraceptive Knowledge, Attitudes and Usage (ii) Contraceptive Services and Cervical Cytology', *Health Trends*, vol. 20, pp. 11–17.

P. McCarron, G. Davey Smith and J. Womersley (1994), 'Deprivation and Mortality in Glasgow: Changes from 1980 to 1992', *British Medical Journal*, vol. 309, pp. 1481–2.

C. McCormack (1993), 'From the Fourth to the Third World – A Common Vision of Health', *Community Development Journal*, vol. 28, pp. 206–17.

A. McCormick, D. Flemming and J. Charlton (1995), *Morbidity Statistics from General Practice: Fourth National Study: 1991-1992, A study carried out by The Royal College of General Practitioners, The Office of Population Censuses and Surveys and The Department of Health*, OPCS series MB5 no. 3, HMSO, London.

D. McFarlane and K. Meier (1993), 'Restructuring Federalism: The Impact of Reagan Policies on the Family Planning Program', *Journal of Health Politics, Policy and Law*, vol. 18, pp. 821–50.

R. McKey, L. Condelli, H. Ganson, B. Barret, C. McConkey, M. Plantz with A. Smith (1985), *The Impact of Head Start on Children, Family and Communities: Final Report of the Head Start Evaluation Synthesis and Utilisation Project*, US Department of Health and Human Services, Publication no. (OHDS)85–31193, Government Printing Office, Washington DC, USA.

P. McLoone and F. Boddy (1994), 'Deprivation and Mortality in Scotland, 1981 and 1991', *British Medical Journal*, vol. 309, pp. 1465–70.

G. Meen (1993), 'Housing and the Economy: An Over-Reliance on Interest Rates?', in Wilcox (ed.) (1993b), pp. 9–11.

G. Meen (1994), *Impact of Higher Rents*, Housing Research Findings no. 109, Joseph Rowntree Foundation, York.

A. Miles (1991), *Women, Health and Medicine*, Open University Press, Milton Keynes.

J. Millar and C. Glendinning (1992), ' "It All Really Starts in the Family": Gender Divisions and Poverty', in Glendinning and Millar (eds.) (1992), pp. 3–10.

J. Morris (1990), 'Inequalities in Health: Ten Years and Little Further On', *The Lancet*, vol. 336, pp. 491–3.

J. Morris, D. Cook and G. Shaper (1994), 'Loss of Employment and Mortality', *British Medical Journal*, vol. 308, pp. 1135–9.

K. Moser, P. Goldblatt and H. Pugh (1990a), 'Occupational Mortality of Women in Employment', in Goldblatt (ed.) (1990a), pp. 130–45.

K. Moser, H. Pugh and P. Goldblatt (1990b), 'Mortality and the Social Classification of Women', in Goldblatt (ed.) (1990a), pp. 146–63.

K. Moser, P. Goldblatt, J. Fox and D. Jones (1990c), 'Unemployment and Mortality', in Goldblatt (ed.) (1990a), pp. 82–99.

M. Murray, A. Swann and G. Clarke (1984), 'Long-Term Effects of a School Based Anti-Smoking Programme', *Journal of Epidemiology and Community Health*, vol. 38, pp. 247–52.

S. Murray, J. Tapson, L. Turnbull, J. McCallum and A. Little (1994), 'Listening to Local Voices: Adapting Rapid Appraisal to Assess Health and Social Needs in General Practice', *British Medical Journal*, vol. 308, pp. 698–700.

NAO (National Audit Office) (1991), *Department of Social Security Support for Lone Parent Families. Report by the Comptroller and Auditor General,* House of Commons Paper no. 153, HMSO, London.

National Federation of Housing Associations (1985), *Inquiry into British Housing: Report, Chaired by HRH The Duke of Edinburgh KG KT,* National Federation of Housing Associations, London.

National Health Strategy (1992), *Enough to Make You Sick: How Income and Environment Affect Health,* National Health Strategy Research Paper no. 1, Department of Health, Housing and Community Services, Canberra, Australia.

NCE (Report of the Paul Hamlyn Foundation National Commission on Education) (1993), *Learning to Succeed: A Radical Look at Education Today and a Strategy for the Future,* Heinemann, London.

NCH (National Children's Home) (1991), *Poverty and Nutrition Survey (1991),* National Children's Home, London.

NCOPF (National Council for One Parent Families) (1994), *Annual Report 1993–94: A Watershed Year for Lone Parents,* National Council for One Parent Families, London.

M. Nelson (1982), 'The Effect of Childbirth Preparation on Women of Different Social Classes', *Journal of Health and Social Behaviour,* vol. 23, pp. 339–52.

S. Newman (1993), *Last in Line: Housing Assistance for Households with Children,* John Hopkins University, USA.

NHSE (National Health Service Executive) (1994a), *HCHS Revenue Resource Allocation: Weighted Capitation Formula,* Department of Health, Leeds.

NHSE (National Health Service Executive) (1994b), *Developing NHS Purchasing and GP Fundholding: Towards a Primary Care-Led NHS,* Department of Health, Leeds.

B. Nolan (1990), 'Socioeconomic Mortality Differentials in Ireland', *The Economic and Social Review,* vol. 21, no. 2, pp. 193–208.

North West Regional Health Authority (1994a), *Patterns of Health: Improving Health in the North West,* North West Regional Health Authority, Warrington.

North West Regional Health Authority (1994b), *1993–Based Small Area Database,* North West Regional Health Authority, Warrington.

P. Nowicki, L. Gintzig, J. Hebel, R. Latham, V. Miller and M. Sexton (1984), 'Effective Smoking Intervention During Pregnancy', *Birth,* vol. 11, pp. 217–24.

D. Nutbeam, M. Wise, A. Bauman, E. Harris and S. Leeder (1993), *Goals and Targets for Australia's Health to the Year 2000 and Beyond,* Australian Government Publishing Service, Canberra.

A. Oakley (1992), *Social Support and Motherhood: The Natural History of a Research Project,* Blackwell, Oxford.

O. O'Donnell and C. Propper (1991), 'Equity and the Distribution of UK National Health Service Resources', *Journal of Health Economics,* vol. 10, pp. 1–19.

OECD (Organisation for Economic Co-operation and Development) (1992), *Economic Outlook,* Organisation for Economic Co-operation and Development, Paris.

D. Olds, C. Henderson, R. Tatelbaum and R. Chamberlin (1986), 'Improving the Delivery of Prenatal Care and Outcomes of Pregnancy: A Randomised Trial of Nurse Home Visitation', *Pediatrics,* vol. 77, pp. 16–28.

D. Olds, C. Henderson, R. Tatelbaum and R. Chamberlin (1988), 'Improving the Life Course Development of Socially Disadvantaged Mothers: A Randomized Trial of Nurse Home Visitation', *American Journal of Public Health,* vol. 78, pp. 1436–45.

B. Ong, G. Humphris, H. Annett and S. Rifkin (1991), 'Rapid Appraisal in an Urban Setting, an Example from the Developed World', *Social Science and Medicine*, vol. 32, no. 8, pp. 909–15.

OPCS (Office of Population Censuses and Surveys) (1978), *Occupational Mortality 1970–72, Decennial Supplement*, HMSO, London.

OPCS (1986a), *Occupational Mortality 1979–80, 1982–83, Decennial Supplement, Part 1 Commentary*, OPCS series DS no. 6, HMSO, London.

OPCS (1986b), *Occupational Mortality 1979–80, 1982–83, Decennial Supplement, Part 2, Microfiche Tables*, OPCS series DS no. 7, HMSO, London.

OPCS (1988), *Occupational Mortality 1979–80, 1982–83, Childhood Supplement*, OPCS series DS no. 8, HMSO, London.

OPCS (1991a), *1991 Census, Local Base Statistics*, Crown Copyright.

OPCS (1991b), *General Household Survey: Cigarette Smoking 1972 to 1990*, OPCS Monitor no. SS91/3, Government Statistical Service, OPCS, London.

OPCS (1992), *Mortality Statistics, Serial Tables: Review of the Registrar General on Deaths in England and Wales, 1841–1990*, OPCS series DH1, no. 25, HMSO, London.

OPCS (1993), 'Tables', *Population Trends*, vol. 74, Winter, pp. 44–68.

C. Oppenheim (1990), *Poverty: The Facts*, Child Poverty Action Group, London.

D. Page (1993), *Building for Communities: A Study of New Housing Association Estates*, Joseph Rowntree Foundation, York.

G. Pappas, S. Queen, W. Hadden and G. Fisher (1993), 'The Increasing Disparity in Mortality Between Socioeconomic Groups in the United States, 1960 and 1986', *New England Journal of Medicine*, vol. 329, no. 2, pp. 103–9.

J. Paris and D. Player (1993), 'Citizen's Advice in General Practice', *British Medical Journal*, vol. 306, pp. 1518–20.

A. Parrott (1994), 'Does Cigarette Smoking Increase Stress?', *Addiction*, vol. 89, pp. 142–4.

A. Parrott, D. Craig and K. Phillips (1993), 'Nicotine Chewing Gum: Patterns of Use During Successful Smoking Cessation', *Proceedings of the Seventh Annual Conference of the European Health Psychology Society*, Brussels Conference Centre, p. 230.

L. Parsons and S. Day (1992), 'Improving Obstetric Outcomes in Ethnic Minorities: An Evaluation of Health Advocacy in Hackney', *Journal of Public Health Medicine*, vol. 14, no. 2, pp. 183–91.

M. Pekurinen (1991), *Economic Aspects of Smoking: Is there a Case for Government Intervention in Finland?*, PhD thesis, University of York, (unpublished).

R. Peto, A. Lopez, J. Boreham, M. Thun and C. Heath (1992), 'Mortality from Tobacco in Developed Countries: Indirect Estimations from National Vital Statistics', *The Lancet*, vol. 339, pp. 1268–78.

M. Petticrew, M. McKee and J. Jones (1993), 'Coronary Artery Surgery: Are Women Discriminated Against?', *British Medical Journal*, vol. 306, pp. 1164–6.

P. Phillimore and A. Beattie (1994), *Health and Inequality in the Northern Region 1981–1991*, Department of Social Policy, University of Newcastle-upon-Tyne, Newcastle-upon-Tyne.

P. Phillimore, A. Beattie and P. Townsend (1994), 'Widening Inequality of Health in Northern England, 1981–91', *British Medical Journal*, vol. 308, pp. 1125–8.

J. Philpott (1994), 'Unemployment, Inequality and Inefficiency: The Incidence and Cost of Unemployment', in Glyn and Miliband (eds.) (1994), pp. 130–44.

R. Pill, J. French, K. Harding and N. Stott (1988), 'Invitation to Attend a Health Check in a General Practice Setting: Comparison of Attenders and Non-Attenders', *Journal of the Royal College of General Practitioners*, vol. 38, pp. 53–6.

A. Piperno and F. Di Orio (1990), 'Social Differences in Health and Utilisation of Health Services in Italy', in Illsley and Svensson (eds.) (1990), pp. 305–12.

S. Platt, C. Martin, S. Hunt and C. Lewis (1989), 'Damp Housing, Mould Growth and Symptomatic Health State', *British Medical Journal*, vol. 298, pp. 1673–8.

S. Pocock, A. Shaper, D. Cook, A. Phillips and M. Walker (1987), 'Social Class Differences in Ischaemic Heart Disease in British Men', *The Lancet*, July 25, pp. 197–201.

J. Popay and M. Bartley (1993), 'Conditions of Formal and Domestic Labour: Towards an Integrated Framework for the Analysis of Gender and Social Class Inequalities in Health', in S. Platt, H. Thomas, S. Scott and G. Williams (eds.), *Locating Health: Sociological and Historical Explorations*, Avebury, Aldershot, pp. 97–120.

C. Power, O. Manor and J. Fox (1991), *Health and Class: The Early Years*, Chapman and Hall, London.

J. Raftery (1993), 'Capitation Funding: Population, Age, and Mortality Adjustments for Regional and District Health Authorities in England, *British Medical Journal*, vol. 307, pp. 1121–4.

RCP (Royal College of Physicians) (1962), *Smoking and Health: A Report on Smoking in Relation to Lung Cancer and Other Diseases*, Pitman Medical, London.

RCP (1971), *Smoking and Health Now: A New Report on Smoking and its Effects on Health*, Pitman Medical, London.

RCP (1994), *Homelessness and Ill Health, Working Party Report*, Royal College of Physicians, London.

R. Reading, A. Colver, S. Openshaw and S. Jarvis (1994), 'Do Interventions that Improve Immunisation Uptake Also Reduce Social Inequalities in Uptake?', *British Medical Journal*, vol. 308, pp. 1142–4.

S. Reijneveld and L. Gunning-Schepers (1994), 'Age, Socioeconomic Status and Mortality at the Aggregate Level', *Journal of Epidemiology and Community Health*, vol. 48, pp. 146–50.

D. Rice (1991), 'Ethics and Equity in the US Health Care: The Data', *International Journal of Health Services*, vol. 21, no. 4, pp. 637–51.

D. Richards (1990), 'Benefits to Health', *Social Work Today*, 26 July, pp. 18–19.

J. Robine and K. Ritchie (1991), 'Healthy Life Expectancy: Evaluation of Global Indicators of Change in Population Health', *British Medical Journal*, vol. 302, pp. 457–60.

D. Robinson and S. Pinch (1987), 'A Geographical Analysis of the Relationship Between Early Childhood Death and Socioeconomic Environment in an English City', *Social Science and Medicine*, vol. 25, no. 1, pp. 9–18.

Y. Robitaille, J. Legault, H. Abbey and I. Pleis (1990), 'Evaluation of an Infant Car Seat Program in a Low-Income Community', *American Journal of Disabled Children*, vol. 144, pp. 74–8.

Y. Rocheron and R. Dickinson (1990), 'The Asian Mother and Baby Campaign: A Way Forward in Health Promotion for Asian Women?', *Health Education Journal*, vol. 49, pp. 128–33.

D. Rodrik (1994), *King Kong meets Godzilla: The World Bank and the East Asian Miracle*, Discussion Paper series no. 944, Centre for Economic Policy Research, London.

R. Rogers (1992), 'Living and Dying in the USA: Sociodemographic Determinants of Death among Blacks and Whites', *Demography*, vol. 29, pp. 287–303.

A. Root (1995), 'Oxford Blues', *Health Service Journal*, 19 January, pp. 32–3.

G. Royston, J. Hurst, E. Lister and P. Stewart (1992), 'Modelling the Use of Health Services by Populations of Small Areas to Inform the Allocation of Central Resources to Larger Regions', *Socioeconomic Planning Sciences*, vol. 26, pp. 169–80.

RUHBC (Research Unit in Health and Behavioural Change) (1989), *Changing the Public Health*, Research Unit in Health and Behavioural Change, John Wiley and Sons, Chichester.

D. Rush (1989), 'Effects of Changes in Protein and Calorie Intake During Pregnancy on the Growth of the Human Foetus', in Chalmers *et al.* (eds.) (1989), pp. 255–80.

D. Rush, J. Alvir, D. Kenny, S. Johnson and D. Horvitz (1988a), 'The National WIC Evaluation: Evaluation of the Special Supplemental Food Program for Women, Infants and Children. III Historical Study of Pregnancy Outcomes', *American Journal of Clinical Nutrition*, vol. 48, pp. 412–28.

D. Rush, D. Horvitz, W. Seaver, J. Leighton, N. Sloan, S. Johnson, R. Kulka, J. Devore, M. Holt, J. Lynch, T. Virag, M. Woodside and D. Shanklin (1988b), 'The National WIC Evaluation: Evaluation of the Special Supplemental Food Program for Women, Infants and Children. IV Study Methodology and Sample Characteristics in the Longitudinal Study of Pregnant Women, the Study of Children and the Food Expenditures Study', *American Journal of Clinical Nutrition*, vol. 48, pp. 429–38.

D. Rush, N. Sloan, J. Leighton, J. Alvir, D. Horvitz, W. Seaver, G. Garbowski, S. Johnson, R. Kulka, M. Holt, J. Devore, J. Lynch, M. Woodside and D. Shanklin (1988c), 'The National WIC Evaluation: Evaluation of the Special Supplemental Food Program for Women, Infants and Children. V Longitudinal Study of Pregnant Women', *American Journal of Clinical Nutrition*, vol. 48, pp. 439–83.

D. Sanders, G. Fowler, D. Mant, A. Fuller, L. Jones and J. Marzillier (1989), 'Randomized Controlled Trial of Anti-Smoking Advice by Nurses in General Practice', *Journal of the Royal College of General Practitioners*, vol. 39, pp. 273–5.

A. Savage (1988), *Warmth in Winter: Evaluation of an Information Pack for Elderly People*, University of Wales College of Medicine Research Team for the Care of the Elderly, Cardiff.

S. Schachter (1978), 'Pharmacological and Psychological Determinants of Smoking', *Annals of Internal Medicine*, vol. 88, pp. 104–14.

J. Schmitt and J. Wadsworth (1994), 'Unemployment, Inequality and Inefficiency: The Rise in Economic Inactivity', in Glyn and Miliband (eds.) (1994), pp. 114–29.

L. Schweinhart, H. Barnes and D. Weikart (eds.) (1993), *Significant Benefits: The High/Scope Perry Preschool Study through Age 27*, High/Scope Press, Ypsilanti, Michigan.

SCOPH (Standing Conference on Public Health) (1994), *Housing, Homelessness and Health, The Standing Conference on Public Health Working Group Report*, The Nuffield Provincial Hospitals Trust, London.

L. Schorr (1988), *Within our Reach: Breaking the Cycle of Deprivation*, Anchor Books, New York.

W. Scott (1991), *Submission to the Select Committee Smoke Free Environment Amendment Bill (no.2)*, New Zealand.

Scottish Office (1992), *Scotland's Health: A Challenge to Us All: A Policy Statement*, HMSO, Edinburgh.

M. Senior (1991), 'Deprivation Payments to GPs: Not What the Doctor Ordered', *Environment and Planning C: Government and Policy*, vol. 9, pp. 79–94.

M. Sexton and J. Hebel (1984), 'A Clinical Trial of Change in Maternal Smoking and its Effects on Birthweight', *Journal of American Medical Association*, vol. 251, pp. 911–15.

T. Sheldon and R. Carr-Hill (1992), 'Resource Allocation by Regression in the National Health Service: A Critique of the Resource Allocation Working Party's Review', *Journal of the Royal Statistical Society (series A)*, vol. 155, pp. 403–20.

T. Sheldon, G. Davey Smith and G. Bevan (1993), 'Weighting in the Dark: Resource Allocation in the New NHS', *British Medical Journal*, vol. 306, pp. 835–9.

T. Sheldon, P. Smith, M. Borwitz, S. Martin and R. Carr-Hill (1994), 'Attempt at Deriving a Formula for Setting General Practitioner Fundholding Budgets', *British Medical Journal*, vol. 309, pp. 1059–64.

R. Skidelsky and L. Halligan (1993), *Beyond Unemployment*, The Social Market Foundation, London.

C. Smaje (1995), *Health, 'Race' and Ethnicity: Making Sense of the Evidence*, King's Fund Institute/Share, London.

P. Smith (1994), 'Institutional Impediments to Improved UK Housing', a paper presented at *Health in Cities conference*, March, Liverpool.

P. Smith, T. Sheldon, R. Carr-Hill, S. Martin, S. Peacock and G. Hardman (1994), 'Allocating Resources to Health Authorities: Results and Policy Implications of Small Area Analysis of Use of In-Patient Services', *British Medical Journal*, vol. 309, pp. 1050–4.

R. Smith (1987), *Unemployment and Health: A Disaster and a Challenge*, Oxford University Press, Oxford.

T. Smith (1993), 'Influence of Socioeconomic Factors on Attaining Targets for Reducing Teenage Pregnancies', *British Medical Journal*, vol. 306, pp. 1232–5.

M. Smyth and F. Browne (1992), *General Household Survey 1990*, OPCS Series GHS no. 21, HMSO, London.

Social Science Research Unit (1994), *An Evaluation of Newpin: A Report by the Social Science Research Unit*, Institute of Education, University of London, London.

D. Spence, J. Hotchkiss, C. Williams and P. Davies (1993), 'Tuberculosis and Poverty', *British Medical Journal*, vol. 307, pp. 759–61.

R. Stern, B. Stilwell and J. Heuston (1989), *From the Margins to the Mainstream: Collaboration in Planning Services with Single Homeless People*, West Lambeth Health Authority, London.

T. Stevenson (1923), 'The Social Distribution of Mortality from Different Causes in England and Wales', *Biometrika*, XV, pp. 382–400.

R. Stone (1945), 'The Analysis of Market Demand', *Journal of the Royal Statistical Society*, vol. 108, pp. 286–382.

D. Strachan (1988), 'Damp Housing and Childhood Asthma: Validation of Reporting of Symptoms', *British Medical Journal*, vol. 297, pp. 1223–6.

Strathclyde Regional Council (1993), *The Social Strategy for the Nineties*, Strathclyde Regional Council, Glasgow.

D. Sweanor (1991), *Canadian Tobacco Tax Project 1985–91*, Non-Smokers Rights Association, Ottawa.

D. Sweanor (1992), *Price and Consumption of Cigarettes, New Zealand 1973–1991*, Non-Smokers Rights Association, Ottawa.

A. Swerdlow (1987), '150 Years of Registrar General's Medical Statistics', *Population Trends*, vol. 48, pp. 20–6.

S. Thake and R. Staubach (1993), *Investing in People: Rescuing Communities from the Margin*, Joseph Rowntree Foundation, York.

M. Thomas, E. Goddard, M. Hickman and P. Hunter (1994), *General Household Survey 1992*, OPCS Series GHS no. 23, HMSO, London.

P. Thornley (1992), 'Liverpool Healthy City: Investing in Community Empowerment', *Community Health Action*, issue 23, Spring, pp. 7–8.

Tobacco Advisory Council (1992), *Tobacco*, May, p. 9.

J. Townsend (1987), 'Cigarette Tax, Economic Welfare and Social Class Patterns of Smoking', *Applied Economics*, vol. 19, pp. 335–65.

J. Townsend (1988), *Price, Tax and Smoking in Europe*, World Health Organization, Copenhagen.

J. Townsend (1993), 'Policies to Halve Smoking Deaths', *Addiction*, vol. 88, pp. 43–52.

J. Townsend, H. Wilkes, A. Haines and M. Jarvis (1991), 'Adolescent Smokers Seen in General Practice: Health, Lifestyle, Physical Measurements and Response to Anti-Smoking Advice', *British Medical Journal*, vol. 303, pp. 947–50.

J. Townsend, P. Roderick and J. Cooper (1994), 'Cigarette Smoking by Socioeconomic Group, Sex and Age: Effects of Price, Income and Health Publicity', *British Medical Journal*, vol. 309, pp. 923–7.

P. Townsend (1987), 'Deprivation', *Journal of Social Policy*, vol. 16, no. 2, pp. 125–46.

P. Townsend and N. Davidson (eds.) (1982), *The Black Report,* in Townsend *et al.* (eds.) (1992), pp. 33–213.

P. Townsend, P. Phillimore and A. Beattie (1988), *Health and Deprivation: Inequality and the North,* Croom Helm Ltd., Kent.

P. Townsend, M. Whitehead and N. Davidson (eds.) (1992), *Inequalities in Health: The Black Report and the Health Divide,* New Edition, Penguin Books, London.

A. Tsouros (ed.) (1991), *World Health Organization Healthy Cities Project: Review of Progress 1987 to 1990,* World Health Organization, Copenhagen.

UNICEF (United Nations Children's Fund) (1993), *The Progress of Nations,* United Nations Children's Fund, New York.

US Department of Health and Human Services (1989), *Reducing the Health Consequences of Smoking. A Report of the Surgeon General.* US Department of Health and Human Services, publication no. CDC 89–8441, Maryland, USA.

US Surgeon General (1986), *The Health Consequences of Involuntary Smoking,* Department of Health and Human Services, publication no. CDC 87–8398, Maryland, USA.

D. Vågerö and O. Lundberg (1989), 'Health Inequalities in Britain and Sweden', *The Lancet,* ii, July 1, pp. 35–6.

T. Valkonen (1993), 'Problems in the Measurement and International Comparisons of Socioeconomic Differences in Mortality', *Social Science and Medicine,* vol. 36, no. 4, pp. 409–18.

N. Wald and A. Nicolaides-Bouman (1991), *UK Smoking Statistics,* 2nd Edition, Oxford University Press, Oxford.

R. Wallace (1993), 'Social Disintegration and the Spread of AIDS-II: Meltdown of Sociogeographic Structure in Urban Minority Neighbourhoods', *Social Science and Medicine,* vol. 37, pp. 887–96.

D. Waller, M. Agass, D. Mant, A. Coulter, A. Fuller and L. Jones (1990), 'Health Checks in General Practice: Another Example of Inverse Care?', *British Medical Journal,* vol. 300, pp. 1115–18.

D. Warburton (1992), 'Smoking Within Reason', *Journal of Smoking-Related Disorders,* vol. 3, pp. 55–9.

K. Warner (1989), 'Effects of the Anti-Smoking Campaign: An Update', *American Journal of Public Health,* vol. 79, pp. 144–51.

Waterloo Health Project (1983), *Six Years of Community Health Struggles,* Waterloo Health Project, London.

S. Webb and S. Wilcox (1991), *Time for Mortgage Benefits,* Joseph Rowntree Foundation, York.

I. Wennemo (1993), 'Infant Mortality, Public Policy and Inequality – A Comparison of 18 Industrialised Countries, 1950–85', *Sociology of Health and Illness,* vol. 15, no. 4, pp. 429–46.

A. White, G. Nicolaas, K. Foster, F. Browne and S. Carey (1993), *Health Survey for England 1991,* OPCS Social Survey Division, HMSO, London.

C. Whitehead and M. Kleinman (1992), *A Review of Housing Needs Assessment,* Housing Corporation, London.

M. Whitehead (1989), *Swimming Upstream: Trends and Prospects in Education for Health,* Research Report no. 5, King's Fund Institute, London.

M. Whitehead (1992), *The Health Divide,* in Townsend *et al.* (eds.) (1992), pp. 219–437.

M. Whitehead and G. Dahlgren (1991), 'What Can Be Done about Inequalities in Health?', *The Lancet,* vol. 338, pp. 1059–63.

M. Whitehead, K. Judge, D. Hunter, R. Maxwell and M. Scheuer (1993), 'Tackling Inequalities in Health: The Australian Experience', *British Medical Journal,* vol. 306, pp. 783–7.

WHO (World Health Organization) (1985), *Targets for Health for All,* World Health Organization, Copenhagen.

WHO (1988), *World Health Statistics Annual*, World Health Organization, Geneva.

WHO (1994), *Health in Europe: The 1993–1994 Health for All Monitoring Report*, World Health Organization, Copenhagen.

S. Wilcox (ed.) (1993a), *Housing Finance Review 1993*, Joseph Rowntree Foundation, York.

S. Wilcox (1993b), *Higher Rents and Work Disincentives*, Housing Research Findings no. 93, Joseph Rowntree Foundation, York.

S. Wilcox (ed.) (1994a), *Housing Finance Review 1994/95*, Joseph Rowntree Foundation, York.

S. Wilcox (1994b), 'The Costs of Higher Rents', in Wilcox (ed.) (1994a), pp. 46–60.

S. Wilcox, G. Bramley, A. Ferguson, J. Perry and C. Woods (1993), *Local Housing Companies: New Opportunities for Council Housing*, Joseph Rowntree Foundation, York.

R. Wilkinson (1992), 'Income Distribution and Life Expectancy', *British Medical Journal*, vol. 304, pp. 165–8.

R. Wilkinson (1993), 'Income and Health', in *Health, Wealth and Poverty: Papers on Inequalities in Income and Health*, Medical World/Socialist Health Association, London, pp. 6–11.

A. Williams (1985), 'Economics of Coronary Artery Bypass Grafting', *British Medical Journal*, vol. 291, pp. 326–9.

R. Windsor, G. Cutter, J. Morris, Y. Reese, B. Manzella, E. Bartlett, C. Samuelson and D. Spanos (1985), 'The Effectiveness of Smoking Cessation Methods for Smokers in Public Health Maternity Clinics: A Randomised Trial', *American Journal of Public Health*, vol. 75, pp. 1389–92.

A. Wohl (1983), *Endangered Lives: Public Health in Victorian Britain*, Methuen, London.

J. Womersley and D. McCauley (1987), 'Tailoring Health Services to the Needs of Individual Communities', *Journal of Epidemiology and Community Health*, vol. 41, pp. 190–5.

C. Woodroffe, M. Glickman, M. Barker and C. Power (1993), *Children, Teenagers and Health: The Key Data*, Open University Press, Milton Keynes.

G. Worgotter and M. Kunze (1986), 'Cigarette Prices and Cigarette Consumption in Austria 1955–83', *New York State Journal of Medicine*, vol. 3, pp. 478–9.

World Bank (1993a), *World Development Report 1993: Investing in Health*, Oxford University Press, New York.

World Bank (1993b), *The East Asian Miracle: Economic Growth and Public Policy*, World Bank, Washington DC.

WRR (Scientific Council for Government Policy) (1991), *Socioeconomic Inequity in Health and Health Policy*, SDU Government Printing Office, The Hague, (in Dutch).

L. Youd and L. Jayne (1986), *Salford Community Health Project: The First Three Years*, Salford Community Health Project, Salford.

Appendix

List of participants, Ditchley Park seminar, 24–26 September 1993

Sir Donald Acheson *Chair*	Visiting Professor in International Health, London School of Hygiene & Tropical Medicine.
Fitzroy Ambursley	Fellow, King's Fund College.
Michaela Benzeval	Senior Research Officer, King's Fund Institute.
Richard Berthoud *Speaker*	Head of Family Finance Group, Policy Studies Institute.
Richard Best *Speaker*	Director, Joseph Rowntree Foundation.
Jonathan Boyce	Associate Director, Health Studies, Audit Commission.
Jacky Chambers	Strategic Commissioning Director, Health Education Authority (now Director of Public Health, North Birmingham Health Authority).
Pam Constantinides	Assistant Director of Public Health, (Research & Development), New River Health Authority.
Anna Coote	Hamlyn Fellow in Social Policy, Institute for Public Policy Research.
Göran Dahlgren *Discussant*	Senior Adviser to Director-General, Swedish International Development Authority.
David Donnison	Emeritus Professor of Town & Regional Planning, Centre for Housing Research, University of Glasgow.
Paul Evans	Clerk, Health Committee, House of Commons (now Deputy Principal Clerk, Public Bill Office).
Peter Flynn	Strategy Management Health Policy Unit, North West Regional Health Authority.
John Fox *Speaker*	Chief Medical Statistician and Deputy Director, Office of Population Censuses and Surveys.
Sally Gooch	Council Member, Royal College of Nursing.
Shirley Goodwin	Associate Director, Hillingdon Health Agency.
Jenny Griffiths	Chief Executive, Hertfordshire Health Agency.
Louise Gunning-Schepers *Discussant*	Professor of Public Health, Institute of Social Medicine, University of Amsterdam.
Chris Ham *Speaker*	Professor of Health Policy & Management, University of Birmingham.

John Howie	Professor of General Practice, University of Edinburgh.
Raymond Illsley *Speaker*	Professorial Fellow in Social Policy, School of Social Sciences, University of Bath.
Feisal Jassat	Co-ordinator, Kirklees Health for All.
Ken Judge	Director, King's Fund Institute.
Julian Le Grand	Titmuss Professor of Health Policy, London School of Economics & Political Science/Professorial Fellow, King's Fund Institute.
Andrew Lyon	Corporate Planner, Glasgow City Council.
Jane Maxwell	Member of Gloucestershire Community Health Council and the Board of Management of Coverage Care.
Robert Maxwell	Secretary & Chief Executive, King Edward's Hospital Fund for London.
Ann Oakley	Director, Social Sciences Research Unit, Institute of Education, University of London.
Ann Parker	Director of Social Services, Berkshire County Council (now based in the Department of Social Policy and Social Work at the University of Manchester).
Dora Pease (observer)	Under Secretary, Health Care Strategy Unit, Department of Health.
Jennie Popay	Professor of Community Health Studies, University of Salford, and Director, Public Health Research & Resource Centre.
Chris Power	Senior Lecturer in Epidemiology & Biostatistics, Institute of Child Health.
Christopher Riley	Associate Director, Welsh Health Planning Forum.
Sue Slipman	Director, National Council for One-Parent Families.
Eleuther Tarimo	Director, Strengthening Health Services, World Health Organization, Geneva.
Nick Timmins	Political Correspondent, *The Independent*.
Joy Townsend *Speaker*	Senior Scientist/Health Economist, Wolfson Institute of Preventive Medicine.
Norman Warner	Chair, City & East London FHSA.
Steven Webb	Programme Director (Personal Sector Research Programme), The Institute for Fiscal Studies.
Margaret Whitehead *Speaker*	Independent Researcher/Visiting Fellow, King's Fund Institute.

Index

access to health care x, xxiii-xxiv, 8, 20, 24, 25, 27, 47, 95,
  101-12, 119
  barriers to xxiv, 20, 39-40, 51, 102, 105-10, 119
  homelessness and 58, 120
  monitoring 8, 101, 105-6; *see also* information systems
  utilisation 102-4, 108
  see also health services
accident prevention 58-9, 66
  child xx, 29, 32, 33, 67, 108, 109, 134
acute services:
  see in-patient services
antenatal care 30, 31, 103, 109
  see also pregnancy
artefact 17, 124
Australia:
  inequalities in health 2, 74
  policies 49, 88, 91

behaviour xviii, xxi, 76
  changing 25, 26, 27, 28-31, 32-3, 50-1, 107;
    see also health education
  health and 18-19, 20, 22, 23
  socioeconomic status and 18, 24
  see also nutrition; smoking
Belgium, inequalities in health 2
benefit uptake xxi, 49, 50, 79, 116, 117, 118, 120, 121
benefits:
  see child benefit; family credit; housing benefit; income
    support; poverty trap; social fund
birth control:
  see family planning
birthweight:
  improving 30, 31
  smoking and 86
  socioeconomic status and 3, 18, 19, 45
Black Report 17, 47, 102, 114
breastfeeding 29, 30, 32
British Regional Heart Study 4, 133

Canada:
  inequalities in health 1, 74
  policies 39, 49, 91, 92
cancer xxii, 10, 14, 82, 86, 87, 91, 134
  see also screening
car ownership:
  access to health care facilities 102, 106
  health and 14, 15, 19, 125, 126
census (UK):
  homelessness 54
  monitoring 105, 113
  occupational class 124
  resource allocation 98, 99, 100
  small area data and health 3, 13, 19, 45, 73
cervical screening:
  see screening
child:
  abuse 32
  mortality 10, 11; *see also* infant mortality
  nutrition of 30, 31, 51, 76
  poverty xxi, 7, 28, 45, 70-2
  smoking 90, 91-2

socioeconomic status and health 2, 3, 12, 17, 33, 35, 58,
  59, 60, 81, 102, 108, 123
  see also accident prevention, child; childcare; education
child benefit xxi, 78-9
child development programme 32
childcare xxiv
  policy options 78, 121, 135, 138-40
  poverty and 138
  provision and cost of 137-8
  see also education, preschool
cigarettes:
  see smoking; tobacco
Commission on Social Justice (CSJ) 134, 135, 136, 137, 140
community based services xxiii, xxiv, 8, 31, 32, 101, 107-11, 119
  see also general practitioners
community care:
  see social care services
community development 25, 33-6, 49, 67, 68, 116
community regeneration xx, 36, 37, 46, 120
coronary heart disease xxii, 10, 18, 31, 58, 82, 86, 87
counselling 34
  debt 49-50
  unemployment 25, 31, 116, 117
  see also social support; work conditions
credit unions 34, 50
cultural values 23, 26

death rates:
  see mortality
Department of Health (DoH) xxiii, 8, 86, 90, 93, 95, 96,
  98, 99, 111, 112, 113, 119, 137
depression 32, 76, 134
  see also mental health; social support
deprivation:
  see material and social circumstances; poverty
deprivation payments:
  see GPs, deprivation payments
determinants of health xix, 4-5, 22-4, 67
  see also inequalities in health, causes
developing countries 38, 43-4, 45
diet:
  see nutrition
disability:
  see morbidity
district health authorities (DHA):
  see health authorities, district

economic activity:
  definition xiii
economic factors:
  see income; poverty
economic growth 23, 42, 43, 45
  see also macroeconomic policies
economic inactivity:
  definition xiii
economic inequality:
  see income distribution
education:
  policy options 129-32, 135
  preschool 39, 51, 129-30; *see also* childcare
  social gradients in attainment 127-8
  status and health 2-3
  unemployment and 128, 129, 132

163